REARRANGING THE WORLD

REARRANGING THE WORLD

Edited by Josephine Balmer
With an introduction by Michèle Roberts

Rearranging the World is a New Audiences inititative of the Arts Council of England, in collaboration with the British Centre for Literary Translation. BCLT, based at the University of East Anglia, works to raise the profile of literary translations through public events, readings, publications and residencies.

First published in paperback in 2001 by
The British Centre for Literary Translation
School of English and American Studies
University of East Anglia
Norwich NR4 7TJ

A New Audiences Project in cooperation with the Arts Council of England and Branching Out. Branching Out works in partnership with public libraries and other organisations to develop new readerships for literature.

Project Coordinator: Catherine Fuller

The British Centre for Literary Translation would like to thank the publishers, authors and translators for their help and cooperation in compiling this anthology

ISBN 0 7145 3080 8

Designed and typeset by Marion Boyars Publishers, London
Printed in England by Mackays of Chatham

Cover and section illustrations are taken from *The Atlas of Experience* by Louise van Swaaij and Jean Klare, published by Bloomsbury in 2000

CONTENTS

Introduction by Michèle Roberts xiii

Editor's Preface xix

Frontispiece: 'Song 7' by Rabindranath Tagore, from *Song Offerings* translated by Joe Winter xxiii

In The Beginning...

Extract from *Life is a Caravanserai* by Emine Sevgi Özdamar, translated by Luise von Flotow 1

'Breastling' by Meg Bateman, from *An Tuil: Anthology of 20th Century Scottish Gaelic Verse* translated by the author and edited by Ronald Black 7

Extract from *Under the Frangipani* by Mia Couto, translated by David Brookshaw 11

Youthful Days 17

Extract from 'At the Pharmacy' by Ioana Ieronim, from *The Triumph of the Water Witch*, translated by Adam J. Sorkin with the author 19

Extract from *Silent Extras* by Arnon Grunberg, translated by Sam Garrett 23

Extract from *Norwegian Wood* by Haruki Murakami, translated by Jay Rubin 31

'A Memory of Childhood' by Don Paterson, from *The Eyes: A version of Antonio Machado* 37

All In A Day's Work 41

Extract from *The Missing Head of Damasceno Monteiro*, by Antonio Tabucchi, translated by J.C. Patrick 43

'Farmhand' by Menna Elfyn, from *Cusan Dyn Dall/Blind Man's Kiss*, translated by Elin ap Hywel 49

Extract from *De Sade's Valet* by Nikolaj Frobenius, translated by Tom Geddes 53

Extract from *The Twins* by Tessa de Loo, translated by Ruth Levitt 59

Extract from *The Adversary: A True Story of Murder and Deception* by Emmanuel Carrère, translated by Linda Coverdale 65

Marriage and Family Life 71

Extract from *The Alphonse Courrier Affair* by Marta Morazzoni, translated by Emma Rose 73

Extract from *The Same Sea* by Amos Oz, translated by Nicholas de Lange 77

'Letter To My Wife' by Miklós Radnóti from *Camp Notebook,* translated by Francis R. Jones 81

Extract from *Losing Eugenio* by Geneviève Brisac, translated by J.A. Underwood 85

'Alienation Through Work' by Karin Kiwus, from *Faint Harps and Silver Voices: Selected Translations*, translated by Christopher Middleton 91

Passionate Affairs 95

'Song 88' by Rabindranath Tagore from *Song Offerings*, translated by Joe Winter 97

Extract from *Les Liaisons Culinaires* by Andreas Staïkos, translated by Anne-Marie Stanton-Ife 101

Extract from the short story 'The Red Coral Bracelet' by Judith Hermann, collected in *The Summerhouse, Later,* translated by Margot Bettauer Dembo 107

Extract from *Our Lady of the Assassins* by Fernando Vallejo, translated by Paul Hammond 113

Extract from *Les Liaisons Culinaires* by Andreas Staïkos, translated by Anne-Marie Stanton-Ife 117

Difficult Times 123

'At the Beginning' by Ioana Ieronim, from *The Triumph of the Water Witch,* translated by Adam J. Sorkin with the author 125

Extract from *The Carpenter's Pencil* by Manuel Rivas, translated by Jonathan Dunne 129

'The war works hard' by Dunya Mikhail, from *A Crack in the Wall: New Arab Poetry*, translated by the author and edited by Margaret Obank and Samuel Shimon 133

Extract from *The 13½ Lives of Captain Bluebear* by Walter Moers, translated by John Brownjohn 137

Extract from *Soul Mountain* by Gao Xingjian, translated by Mabel Lee 143

Calm Old Age 149

'The Eyes' by Don Paterson, from *The Eyes: A version of Antonio Machado* 151

Extract from *Portrait in Sepia* by Isabel Allende, translated by Margaret Sayers Peden 155

Extract from *Dirty Havana Trilogy* by Pedro Juan Gutiérrez, translated by Natasha Wimmer 161

'Cat Out of Hell' by Menna Elfyn, from *Cusan Dyn Dall/Blind Man's Kiss,* translated by Gillian Clarke 167

...And In the End 171

'Postcard (4)' by Miklós Radnóti, from *Camp Notebook,* translated by Francis R. Jones 173

Extract from *As the Crow Flies* by Véronique Tadjo, translated by Wangũi wa Goro 177

Extract from *Dunyazad* by May Telmissany, translated by Roger Allen 181

Extract from *Death and the Penguin* by Andrey Kurkov, translated by George Bird 187

Endpiece: 'Wait' by Faraj Bou al-Isha, translated by Khaled Mattawa from *A Crack in the Wall: New Arab Poetry,* edited by Margaret Obank & Samuel Shimon 191

Authors' Details 195

Translators' Details 201

Permissions, Acknowledgements and Complete list of Featured Books 205

Editors' Details 209

"...Reading this book you get the excitement of venturing into the unknown, all the surprises of travelling, and the pleasures of recognition. Most of all, perhaps, you get the joy of recognising how important the human imagination is, how without it we would fail utterly to understand each other and so would wither and perish..."

Michèle Roberts

INTRODUCTION

One world. One race: the human race.

Our closeness and similarity to each other is something to celebrate. But our differences are too. Global culture doesn't have to mean only that we all consume the same artefacts, wear the same trainers, eat the same burgers in buns. Increasingly – thanks to ongoing developments in information technology, air travel, tourism – we can explore what we haven't got in common, learn about each other's cuisines, histories, clothes, ways of dancing and driving and shopping and making love. Armchair travel happens in front of a screen, with your headphones on. Samplers of world music are easily available. So why not a sampler of world literature? Here it is.

I recommend this book simply for the deep interest of the writing in it and the great pleasure that reading it brings. It is new and different and fun.

The sampler form really works for books. You can make your own mix. You don't have to read through this book from beginning to end. That's perfectly possible, of course. The material in this anthology is arranged in seemingly chronological form, tracking human existence, in all its diversity, from birth to childhood to adulthood. That's a pattern that satisfies our hunger for stories, our desire to know what happened next, for narratives that make sense of a chaotic and dazzling world. You can follow this route and enjoy the way that one section of extracts chimes against another, journeying around the world as you journey through a life, through novels and stories and poems. Or you can double back and forth as though you're playing hide and seek, dip in and out at random, following your nose, following your whim. If you are interested in a particular country, you might want to start reading a piece that comes from there. Or you might decide to read all the poems first. Or all the extracts from novels.

This ducking and diving is, of course, one of the pleasures of reading. Not just this sampler but any book. It's up to you, the reader, to choose, minute by minute, exactly how to do it, whether to read every word or to skim and skip, whether to start at the end, check the middle, then begin again at the beginning. Literature, in this sense, is highly interactive, dependent on an active reader; an aggressive reader. If you want to hurl the book across the room and storm crossly out, no-one's going to tick you off or stop you. You don't have to be docile and good and passive to read a book. You read with all of your passionately-responding self.

On the other hand, you can simultaneously enjoy all the pleasures of passivity too. Think of the images we use for a good read. I was carried away. I was somewhere else. I was enraptured. I was transported. Reading can offer all the delights of seduction, of being led astray, enticed somewhere new and exciting and disturbing. Reading is like falling in love. A subversive and sexy feeling of frissons and thrills and deep satisfactions and hunger for more. In some cultures, some of the time, reading, like writing, can also be seen politically as provocative and dangerous. Such is the power of the word. But, to stick with my theme of frivolity and pleasure, reading is a habit, an indulgence, that will not make you fat or drunk or addict you to the wrong sort of drugs or get you told off for adultery. So there is a lot to be said for it. It is certainly powerful, despite seeming so innocent. Writing a book may not change the world but it may change the reader. Hence the anxieties of censors to check our imaginings. Hence the sensation of bliss when you come to the end of a good book and you stagger, dazed, back to normality.

I think reading is not only important but one of the greatest pleasures in my life and so spend as much time as possible every day doing it. As a child, my great fear was running out of books to read, that I'd read all the books in the world available to me at home, school and the public library. I don't worry about that anymore, since I know I can travel further afield, on legs or online, to the library or the bookshop to stock up, but I do sometimes wonder what to read next. The child's cry of 'what shall we play now?' turns into the grown-up's plaint, 'what shall I read now?' I enjoy friends recommending books they have enjoyed, since I don't always feel sure how to find the next book I shall want to read.

Perhaps this is especially true when it comes to foreign literature. We British have not always felt confident about finding and reading authors from across the world. Our island mentality got in the way, and perhaps our imperial past, and perhaps a more emotional feeling, too, of fear of too much pleasure, fear of difference, fear of the unknown and the strange. Fear of change. Fear of being seduced and led astray and enjoying it too much. Then there was the simple practical problem of not being able to find the books in the shops, either because they hadn't been translated into English and published over here, or because they were hidden in a dark corner or somehow otherwise unavailable.

How much the situation has altered. As we British start to become, for fascinating historical reasons, strange to ourselves, to wonder what it really means to be British and what that word includes, to desire to travel abroad, to discover a new curiosity both about our own identity and that of others, so we start to realize that foreign authors are not nearly as difficult and automatically highfalutin as we had supposed.

This sampler is a brilliant example of how to tackle these difficulties. It acts like a good friend introducing us to new paths through the library and the bookshop, new ways to browse. It opens our eyes and minds to the fact that an enormous variety of fiction and poetry is published abroad just as it is here. If you like thrillers, for example, as I do, then you can suddenly wake up to the fact that there are masses of them out there, and now at last you can taste one in English. Perhaps reading in English, in translation, calms and tames our prejudices? The writers you will meet in this collection are human beings, just like you and me, with similar rages and passions and doubts and fears. It is a book that does far more for international relations than politicians' speeches or tourist brochures ever could.

This book is also a testimony to the often unsung and overshadowed labours of love of translators. They are truly writers, truly makers. Without them, we couldn't approach this exciting new world of literature. Translation is often assumed to be invisible. A good translation, the wisdom goes, should be quietly unnoticeable. Faithful too, like a good wife. I don't agree. While a deft translation will be in the fittest possible, the most appropriate English, yet I wouldn't want it to iron out all the cultural idiosyncrasies of its original. To continue with the gendered metaphor, I like a translation that has obviously been around, travelled a bit, lived a little. I like a translation that lets you see where it has come from, that precisely does not pretend that all over the world we all eat the same burgers in the same buns, but that, in fact, draws us into new places, new experiences.

A good translation makes the reader rejoice in the difference of the culture being presented, as well as simultaneously making the reader feel at home in it. Translation is a form of magic. One text gets changed into another. Metamorphosis and transformation happen because of translation. As one book changes into another, new one, so the reader is changed by absorbing it. The root of translation is the Latin for being carried across. Back to that experience of rapture again, of being snatched up and whirled off into new lands, of yielding to the unknown and going delightfully out of control.

Reading for me as a child was my way of practising leaving home and having adventures, a way into the real world, not just the inner world of fantasy, but the world outside the house and the home, a world of delicious dangers. Reading connected the inner world to the outer. Reading was the way that I could contact the imagination of others. These people might be dead, or have no names, but that didn't matter; reading let you leap through time and space, all because of the magic and transforming powers of language. I loved translations without realizing that is what they were. I devoured, for example, books of fairy tales translated from Irish, Welsh, Scottish and Breton sources, books of folk tales translated from different languages from all over India and China. I was lucky to find such books in the children's section of our local public library. I still vividly remember some of those stories, which helped form my imagination.

Reading this sampler of world literature has given me back those pleasures of childhood, plus something else. It has made me realize how we all translate ourselves to each other, all of the time. We do this in families, between lovers, between friends. So translation seems to be a major image of how we function in the world as people wanting to understand each other. Them and us just won't do. We're all foreigners and we're all at home. Reading this book you get the excitement of venturing into the unknown, all the surprises of travelling, and the pleasures of recognition. Most of all, perhaps, you get the joy of recognizing how important the human imagination is, how without it we would fail utterly to understand each other and so would wither and perish.

I wish you a very happy time reading this sampler.

Michèle Roberts

EDITOR'S PREFACE

One of the observations most often made about translated literature is how little of it is published in Britain, around five per cent of all new books at a conservative estimate. Working on this project, however, it was hard not to feel a great sense of optimism. For weeks packages arrived daily from participating publishers and out would tumble another hefty – and exciting – pile of books: crime fiction, thrillers, historical fiction, short stories, novellas, humorous or romantic novels, not to mention new collections and anthologies of poetry. All in all, there was plenty, too, to banish another common preconception about literature in translation: that it's difficult, even inaccessible. Here were books you could pick up as easily as any of the more familiar names on the shelves, books which offered the lyricism of Louis de Bernières, the wit of Nick Hornby or Helen Fielding, the historical sensibilities of Peter Ackroyd, the grittiness of Irvine Welsh, as well as the high seriousness of Jeanette Winterson or the engaging eccentricity of Iain Sinclair.

When it came to whittling down such a plethora of possibilities to the extracts collected here, I was looking for works that illustrated both how universal our experiences might be across the globe and also how culturally diverse – a search which lead to the collection's structure, grouped as a journey through life from birth to death. Childbirth, motherhood, passion, illness or bereavement might feel the same in any language but geographical and cultural forces do play their part; we can all empathize with a small child embarrassed by a *faux pas* made in front of adults, but how much more serious is this when the setting is communist Romania, as in Ioana Ieronim's poem 'At the Pharmacy'? We might sympathize, too, with the ravages of passing time but there is an added poignancy to the plight of the elderly clinging on to their dreams of better times as they face a poverty-stricken old age in Castro's Cuba, as Pedro Juan Gutiérrez's *Dirty Havana Trilogy* recounts.

Historical conditions, too, have their role. These novels and poems offer us unique glimpses of some of the most important events of recent times; the fate of Galician Republican prisoners in the Spanish Civil War, as in Manuel Rivas's *The Carpenter's Pencil*. Or the plight of forced labourers in Nazi Germany, seen from the viewpoint of both conqueror, as in Tessa de Loo's Dutch bestseller, *The Twins*, and conquered, as in Miklós Radnóti's extraordinary poetry collection *Camp Notebook*. We also have a front-row seat as the Iron Curtain falls across the Eastern bloc or the former USSR disintegrates; as the Cultural Revolution sweeps through China, or the Gulf conflict ignites the Middle East – seen here unusually, in Dunya Mikhail's poem 'The war works hard', from an Iraqi viewpoint.

Of course, all these books have already been a great success in their own countries, winning literary prizes or even becoming huge best-sellers. There are internationally acclaimed authors, too, such as Gao Xingjian, the 2000 Nobel Prize Winner, or Marta Morazzoni, winner of the 2001 Independent Foreign Fiction Prize for *The Alphonse Courrier Affair*. But what strikes most is their willingness to break rules, to cross fixed boundaries. And so we find a Norwegian, Nikolaj Frobenius, writing an historical novel about eighteenth-century France and the Marquis de Sade, or Antonio Tabucchi's *The Missing Head of Damasceno Monteiro,* an Italian crime novel about a Lisbon reporter working on a story in Oporto. These are books which regularly confound all expectations and prejudices; Emine Sevgi Özdamar's raucous, earthy account of growing up as a woman in Turkey, Haruki Murakami's frank memories of the late 1960s sexual revolution among Tokyo students or Colombian Fernando Vallejo's vision of harsh reality, rather than magical realism, in South America. They are also books which present compelling challenges – and rewards – to their translators. But through the alliance of author and translator, the heady mix of original and translation, in one way or another, they all, to quote Khaled Mattawa's translation of Libyan poet Faraj Bou al-Isha ,'rearrange the world'.

Josephine Balmer

Into my life come new, come new,
in smell, in colour, in song too;
come in body, come in mind;
come in touch of thrilling kind;
in joy, in sleep's spell come: O you
into my life come new, come new.

Come the beautiful, bright and graceful,
the pure and splendid, and the peaceful;
in form of vast and various law;
in pain, in pleasure, and at heart's core.
Come in all daily tasks: O you
come at the end of what we do…
into my life come new, come new.

'Song 7'
from *Song Offerings* by Rabindranath Tagore,

translated from Bengali by Joe Winter

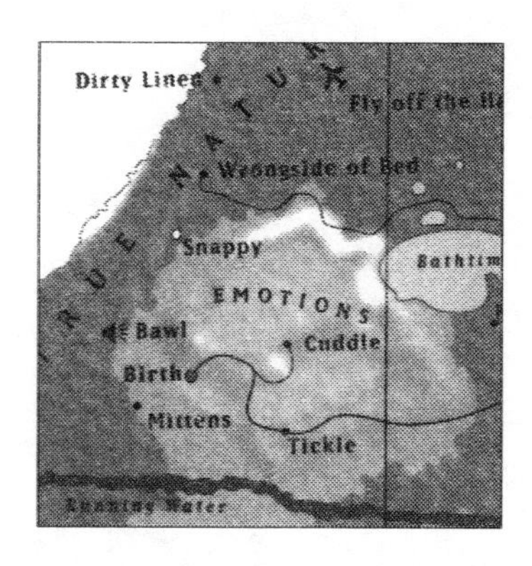

IN THE BEGINNING...

From *Life is a Caravanserai • Has Two Doors • I Came in One • I Went Out the Other*
by Emine Sevgi Özdamar,

Translated from German by LUISE VON FLOTOW
Middlesex University Press

Hailed by John Berger as the one of the most original novels about Turkey, and particularly Turkish women, ever written, Emine Sevgi Özdamar's *Life is a Caravanserai* tells the story of a young girl growing up in the politically turbulent Turkish society of the 1950s and 1960s. Written in German, its raunchy, raucous language belies Western assumptions about women in the Eastern world. In this extract, as her pregnant mother travels on a train filled with soldiers through a strife-torn Turkey, our narrator makes her first entrance into the world, disconcerting her family from the start.

...Translating Özdamar's German meant dealing with the relatively naïve and earthy language of an immigrant Turkish guestworker in Germany. It's a writing based on Özdamar's literal translations of Turkish metaphors, proverbs, colloquialisms, and prayers, and so my translation approach was to try to stay as literal as she is. It also meant giving literal versions of the scatological language of the child-narrator and her parents and friends. There was no reason to 'clean up' or otherwise produce euphemistic versions of that earthy speech, so reminiscent of the immigrant worker who learns the new language on the construction site rather than at the university...

Luise von Flotow on translating
Life is a Caravanserai

First I saw the soldiers, I was standing there in my mother's belly between the bars of ice, I wanted to hold on and grabbed the ice and slipped and landed in the same spot, knocked on the wall, nobody heard.

The soldiers took off the coats that had so far been worn by 90,000 dead and not yet dead soldiers. The coats stank of 90,000 dead and not yet dead soldiers and were already hanging on the hooks. One soldier said, 'Make room for the pregnant woman!'

The hair of the woman standing next to my mother had turned white overnight because she heard her brother was dead. She only had one brother, and a husband she didn't love. Later in life I called this woman 'Cotton Aunt', and every now and then when I opened the door to her she'd say, 'Girl, you were a little shit in your mother's belly when I handed you and your mother over to the soldiers in the train.'

Cotton Aunt told the soldiers, 'Protect this woman like your own eyes. Her husband is a soldier too, she's returning to her father's house for the birth. If you carry this innocent woman back to her father, and hold her over your heads, then Allah will also carry your mothers and sisters over his head.'

The train screamed, Cotton Aunt got out and called into the train window, 'Fatmaaaa nobody stays inside, they all come out. But wait until you're in your father's house!' The train departed.

At that time the journey was simple, nobody knew the names of the mountains or the rivers, we knew the train is called the 'black train' and all the soldiers are called Mehmet and when they're sent to war they're called Mehmetçik. The 'black train' was used to fetch them out of their mothers' wombs and send them, heads shaved, into the empty fields. Up, down, fire. 'Onion,' yelled the captain, that means left, 'Garlic,' yelled the captain, that means right, and evening means cleaning the captain's wooden floor.

Inside the belly I thought my father is a soldier too, his coat probably stinks like these coats. Later I'll be the stinkfather daughter...

...The train stopped. My mother opened her eyes, across from her were four soldiers, all of them holding cigarettes between their thumb and forefinger, smoking, wrapped in their damp wet coats, silent, and looking at the pregnant woman. There was a knock at the window. The water vendor. The first soldier pulled down the window, bought some water, gave it to my mother, my mother drank it, in her belly I said, there's so much water here, I'm drowning here, without ever having seen my father, give me something to eat. No food came, I bit into a cord and saw that my mother was also biting down hard onto her lip. A soldier opened his eyes wide, 'What's wrong sister? Is something wrong?' My mother said, 'No, it's cold in here.' In her belly I said, it's cold and dark and wet in here too. And there's so much stuff I keep bumping my head against. The soldiers closed the window and spread a soldier's coat over my mother's belly. I lost consciousness and only woke up one August morning and cried immediately. I wanted to go back to the water room and see the film with the soldiers again, the film, was torn, where did the soldiers go?

The new room was very light and very high, many women were sitting around, and a bee looked in the window, at me, at my legs. My mother said, 'She's sticking her legs out of the wrap again. My father doesn't like newborn children because they look like cat babies, but when he walked by he just happened to glance in the direction of this baby, and his eyes stayed on the baby, and he said, "Aman, Fatma what a lovely child that is."' After she said this, the women left. They climbed up onto the flat roof and spread grain on the cotton sheets to dry. All five women were my grandfather's wives, the mother of my mother was the only one who wasn't there, because she had to die young. While the women were spreading out the grain on the sheets, I saw their backsides like five full moons glued side by side, moving up and down. As the birds were waiting in the sky near the grain, unafraid of the women, and looking into the women's eyes, my mother looked at one of the birds and thought, maybe this bird is my dead mother, she's hungry and doesn't have a tongue to say so. And so Fatma began to cry. I cried very loud too, and my mother closed my mouth and opened wide her eyes, and looked into my eyes, and said, 'Don't cry, don't cry. People shouldn't hear children crying in a house where there's no man!' That made me cry even louder and my mother gave me a slap on my mouth. Just at this moment, the bee that had spotted me through the window and was getting ready to land on the corner of my mothermilk sweet mouth, collided with my mother's hand. It stung her. The bee died, my mother cried out the window, 'Mother, I'm on fire!' and the five women on the roof said in chorus, 'Every woman's on fire if her husband has been a soldier for four years.'

‘Breastling’
by Meg Bateman,

translated from Gaelic by the author
Collected in **An Tuil: Anthology of 20th Century Scottish Gaelic Verse**, edited by RONALD BLACK
Polygon

Meg Bateman is part of the renaissance of Gaelic poetry in Scotland over the last hundred years, particularly among women poets. ‘Breastling’ treats a simple domestic scene between mother and child with poignancy and tenderness – as well as an underlying hint of menace.

Breastling

In the grey of the dawn
you drink intently,
your eyes gaze ahead,
their brownness tells me nothing;
there is authority in the hold
of your two hands on the breast,
your toes knead my belly
to a rhythm of their own.

In the evening you grow fond:
you press in the nipple
and laugh as it rises,
peeping round at Dad
with a biscuit in your fist.

But at night
no tamed pup you –
no kiss on the lips can soothe you
or ditty whispered in your ear –
your fingers tear at my gown
as, roaring at the darkness,
you claim your hereditary right.

From *Under the Frangipani*
by Mia Couto

Translated from Portuguese by DAVID BROOKSHAW
Serpent's Tail

Under the Frangipani, a new novel from Mia Couto, Mozambique's most prominent writer, is set in a former Portuguese fort, once a storehouse for slaves and ivory and now a refuge for old people including Navaia Caetano, an old man-child cursed by an evil spirit. When a murder is committed at the fort, Caetano tells the strange story of his birth to investigating police officer Izidine.

I'll begin by talking about my mother. I've never known such a fertile woman. How many times did she jump the moon? She produced many a child. Yes, I mean just that: child, not children. For she would always give birth to the same creature. When she bore a new child, the previous one would disappear. But all the ones who followed were identical, drops feeding the same water. Folk in the village suspected punishment, some failure to obey the old laws. So what was the reason for such punishment? No one spoke out loud, but everyone knew the reason for the curse: my father was always visiting my mother's body. He wasn't patient enough to wait while my mother was producing her milk. That was what tradition required: a woman's body is untouchable during her first milk. My old man disobeyed. He himself boasted he'd found a way round the obstacle. He would take a magic string with him on his love-makings. When he was ready to knead his wife, he would tie a knot round the child's waist. Love could then take place without any consequences.

My mother's tainted fate was thus apparently sealed. I stress the word 'apparently', because my own tragedy began at that point. I know that now: I was born from one of those badly-tied knots around the waist of a dead brother.

Don't worry, inspector, I'm getting to myself. Don't you remember what I said? I was born into a fragile little body, always spared from thirst. My arrival seemed to have been blessed: the six seeds of the *hacata* had been cast. They had fallen well, aligned by good spirits.

This child will be more ancient than life itself.

My grandfather lifted me up to be blessed and held me aloft. He did not speak, as if he were weighing my soul. Who knows what he was seeking? Among the thousands of living creatures, only man listens to silences. Then my grandfather clasped me to his chest, once again full of laughter. But he was deceived in his joy. I lay under a curse. I was made aware of this curse the first few times I cried. As I wept, I began to disappear. My tears washed away my bodily matter, dissolved my substance. But that wasn't the only sign of my condition. Before that, I had been born free of my mother's labour. As I left her body, she suffered no pains, for I was devoid of substance. I slid through her belly, drained from my mother's flesh, more liquid than blood itself.

My mother then had a prediction that I was heaven's gift. She called my father, who lowered his eyes, because a man is forbidden to face his son until the umbilical cord has fallen. My old man sent for the soothsayer, who sniffed my spirits, sneezed, coughed and then gave his prognosis.

This child must not suffer any sadness. Any sadness, however slight, will be doubly fatal.

My old man nodded, pretending he understood. It looks bad for a man to ask another to explain his words. It was my mother who confessed she didn't understand.

What I'm saying, mother, is that if the child cries, he may never reappear.

Is one tear enough?

Less than one. The merest fleck of a tear is enough.

Tears were confirmation of my childhood, denying my aged body. The soothsayer was once again seized by convulsions. The spirits were speaking through his mouth but, before that, it was as if they were crossing the deepest recesses of my flesh. The soothsayer's powerful voice continued, now hoarse, now chanting. It poured out its sentences and increased its pitch in spasms. Sometimes it was a mere trickle, without any body to it. Other times, it was a torrent startled by its own grandiloquence.

I was more newly-fledged than fledgling, but I could already understand everything I heard. The medicine man asked me something in Ndau, a language I didn't know, and still don't know. But someone inside me took over my voice and answered in that strange tongue. When the soothsayer cast the bones, they told him I should wear a *tsungulo*. He put the string of cloth beads round my neck. I didn't know this, but wrapped inside the cloth were the remedies against sadness. This charm would defend me against time.

Now, go.

And he explained: those words were keys that broke inside the locks once the doors had been opened. They couldn't be used a second time. My mother fell silent and, lost in her own thoughts, dragged me homewards.

Mother: what illness have I got?

My mother squeezed me hard. Never again would I feel such strength in her hand.

I can't talk about it, my son.

She seemed to be on the verge of tears. But no, she just turned her face away. And she walked off, head bowed. I inherited this way of growing sad from my mother: only when I'm not crying do I believe in my tears. At that moment, only my uncle Taúlo could reveal the cause of my sufferings to me.

You, my little Caetano, you have no age.

So that's how it was: I had been born, grew up and reached my dotage all on the same day. A person's life stretches out over years, like a parcel being slowly unwrapped, but which never falls into the hands of the person it's intended for. My life, on the other hand, had been spent in just one day. In the morning, I was an infant, kittenishly crawling around on all fours. In the afternoon, I was a grown man, confident in my step and my speech. At night, my skin was already growing wrinkled, my voice fading, and I was pained by regret at not having lived my life.

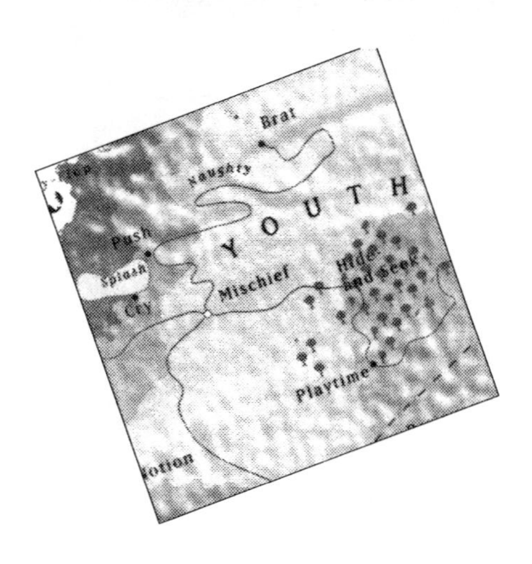

YOUTHFUL DAYS

From **'At the Pharmacy'**
collected in *The Triumph of the Water Witch* by Ioana Ieronim

Translated from Romanian by ADAM J. SORKIN with the author
Bloodaxe Books

In *The Triumph of the Water Witch* Romanian poet Ioana Ieronim remembers her childhood in the Transylvanian Saxon part of Rasnov, a small town in the Carpathians. Through a series of prose-poems, she laments the loss of a once-thriving community destroyed by the imposition of Soviet-style communism, viewing the peculiarities and dangers of life under its regime through a child's eyes, as, for example, when she is puzzled by the statues of Lenin and Marx in one of her local stores.

At the Pharmacy

'But how do they eat?' I asked my mother. Silently, the people in line looked at me.

Mama turned her head away. I couldn't see her face.

'Mama!' A pull at her sleeve. 'Tell me, tell me, those up there, how do they eat?' My mother, I think, ordered me to shut up. Some people near us smiled, their faces directed downward. No one uttered a word.

It was the first time I'd asked that question, although I'd wondered about it for quite some time: there on the wall of the pharmacy, since they were portrayed with beards disguising their mouths, how could they ever eat? Each one separately framed. (MARXENGELSLENINSTALIN they were labelled beneath them. Anyway, I couldn't read yet.)

Then my mother turned back to me and I caught sight of her face once more – my words froze.

But I couldn't understand what I'd done wrong, how I might learn to avoid it some other time. When we were by ourselves, Mama explained to me, 'You never know who might be near you...' My mother's voice drew black furrows across us both. Waves of darkness filled the silence.

There's a crossroads where you meet the Devil in the guise of a beardless youth, the cunning little old woman, the wicked dwarf. A crossroads where the big dread comes out to greet you. It has no face. It never eats, but it gets fat. It will be your close companion. As heavy as earth. Beneath your ribs. Travelling, travelling on your bony shoulders.

From *Silent Extras*
by Arnon Grunberg

Translated from Dutch by SAM GARRETT
Secker & Warburg

Arnon Grunberg's comic, heart-breaking novel *Silent Extras* details the adventures of three young friends – Ewald, Broccoli and Elvira – who together plan 'Operation Brando', a scheme to exchange their drab, mundane lives in Amsterdam for fame and fortune in Hollywood, their dreams undampened by their lack of success – or talent. Here, Ewald, the story's narrator, attempts to be accepted at stage school.

As an American translator of Dutch I had a problem with some of the references; I couldn't place 'It-Ain't-Half-Hot-Mum' at all. It was only when an Australian friend who was also translating the book and had seen the show told me about it that it fell into place – as a translator you sometimes rely on others working within the variations of the English language to help you…

Sam Garrett on translating
Silent Extras

On my seventeenth birthday I went to Maastricht to audition for the theatre school. I'd heard that the best theatre school was the one in Maastricht.

I stayed at the Hotel de la Bourse. The place was full of travelling salesmen. At eight o'clock in the morning, the chambermaid knocked on the door and yelled in three languages that she was coming in to mop the floor. Even if you shouted: 'No, I'm naked', she still came in.

It was June, and it was hot. I was wearing some shorts I'd bought at Sissy-Boy just before I left. I remembered that the mod girls at school always bought their clothes there. The shorts were three sizes too big for me, but the salesman told me it was the fashion that summer to walk around in oversized shorts.

'So, young man, I see you're also wearing *It-Ain't-Half-Hot-Mum* pants?' was the first thing the drama teacher in Maastricht said to me. The term '*It-Ain't-Half-Hot-Mum* pants' didn't say much to me, so I just smiled amiably.

The second day in Maastricht they locked up all the boys in a little classroom and made us undress. The only thing we were allowed to keep on was our underpants. The girls were locked in another classroom. The teachers came and took us away one by one.

When it was my turn, a man came and led me to the gym. I walked along beside him, through the halls of the Maastricht theatre school, in my underpants. I realized then that people with clothes on have a giant edge on the naked or partly nude.

Two women and a man were sitting at a table in the gym. The man was in the middle. He was wearing glasses and had bristly white hair. He stared at me for a minute. He didn't say a word. I started thinking maybe something weird was stuck to my body, so I looked at myself as inconspicuously as possible, but I couldn't see anything. Fortunately, the two women weren't staring at me. They were looking out the window and yawning. Finally, I had to walk up to the table and say my name loud and clear.

'Ewald Stanislas Krieg,' I said.

'Stanislas-Krieg, is that a compound surname?' the man asked.
'No,' I said, 'Ewald Stanislas is a compound first name.'

The man wrote something down. Then he came out from behind the table and started pinching my Achilles' tendons. I told him it tickled. He didn't seem to be listening. After a couple of minutes he must have figured he'd messed with my legs long enough.

'Jump, Ewald Stanislas,' he said.

'Ewald, just Ewald, that's plenty.'

'Jump,' he said.

I jumped.

'Higher,' the man said.

I jumped higher.

'Higher than that,' the man said.

I jumped even higher. I was starting to feel like some kind of frog. But the man just kept shouting: 'Higher, higher.' I wondered why you had to break the high-jump record when all you wanted was to be an actor.

When the man figured I'd jumped enough, he said: 'Now walk a diagonal line.'

I walked diagonally.

He made me walk three more diagonals.

Finally, one of the women at the table said: 'T.U.'

I asked what that meant, and she told me: 'Technically Unfit.'

'Well, thanks for all your time,' I said.

'Thank you for your time,' said the man who'd pinched my Achilles' tendons. I left the gym. The next candidate was already waiting in his underpants.

The next day was the singing test. I had to sing part of an opera with a lady, tête-à-tête. The lady was in her late eighties and had curly red hair.

'Stanislas,' the lady said, 'that's an unusual name; it sounds like Stanislavsky. You know Stanislavsky, I take it?'

'Vaguely,' I said, 'vaguely, we never actually met.'

'Stanislavsky, the great dramatic innovator,' the lady said.

I didn't know any opera songs. So she sang something for me. I had to sing along with her. That was hard. I kept thinking about how my breath smelled.

'No,' she said, 'if you're going to sing you have to open your mouth. Open your mouth, open it. There are more than two hundred candidates waiting for me.'

The lady put her ear to my lips and I had to make all kinds of sounds. An 'ooh' and an 'aaay' and a 'hoo-hoo' and a 'low ooo' and 'one from the diaphragm' and an 'ooo' that caught in my throat.

At one point, she wanted to look down my throat.

A few minutes later she said: 'T.U.'

I kept going to classes for the rest of the week, even though I knew my chances of being accepted were minimal. The organizers urged us to get to know other aspiring actors and actresses, but I couldn't even keep up a conversation with them.

I lived in great fear of all the people walking around at the Maastricht Theatre School. A fear so great that I had to hurl myself through the gates of the school every morning with total disregard for life and limb. It was a huge struggle for me not to stay in the dark at the Hotel de la Bourse, where at least I didn't have to jump up and down in my underpants like a frog. I probably only stuck it out for that week because my father had said: 'Doing your best isn't enough. When you die, you have to be able to say: "I didn't succeed, but God knows I did all I could. It wasn't my fault."'

In the evening I wandered around Maastricht and, at my father's expense, ate in fancy restaurants where I sometimes pretended to be of poor but noble lineage. My fellow aspiring actors ate in the cafeteria and hung around in bars I didn't dare to enter. After dinner I'd lock myself in my hotel room and spend wildly passionate nights with myself. I even made love to myself in the bathtub. By way of experiment, I resolved to have an underwater orgasm every night. Sometimes my fingers still smelled of my own seed the next morning, but since I was the only one who smelled my fingers, that didn't seem like much of a problem.

Once, in the cafeteria of the Maastricht Theatre School, I told an aspiring actor: 'You know, my sperm's been black for the last couple of weeks. Everything that comes out looks like tar. Do you think I should see a doctor?'

All right, maybe it wasn't such a great joke, but at least I was trying. From that day on, the aspiring actor and his friends gave me a wide berth. I've never told anyone that my sperm is black ever again.

The younger, healthier and happier they were, the more I feared them. The Maastricht Theatre School was crawling with the young, healthy and happy. All Maastricht was crawling with young, healthy and happy people, with the exception of the cleaning lady who burst into my room every morning at eight.

On the last day we had to recite a monologue and a poem in the school auditorium. I recited a completely incomprehensible poem by Boudewijn Büch. I'd come across it in an issue of *Avenue*, and I thought it was very deep. After that I did a monologue from a Greek tragedy. Halfway through the monologue, I got very bad stomach cramps.

During that week in Maastricht, I'd had my first experience with shrimp: king prawns, to be exact. I'd been raised in the conviction that I should only eat fish if it had fins and scales, things like cod, flounder, halibut and carp to name a few. Squid, shrimp, mussels and oysters were off-limits. My family stuck pretty strictly to the dietary laws. Not that anyone at our house believed in God. We clung to the laws because our ancestors had.

I was convinced that these stomach cramps were the hand of God, wreaking vengeance for the prawns I'd eaten the night before. During the monologue, my thoughts were pretty much fixed on prawns, but no one seemed to notice.

Later that same summer, I went on a one-week diet of mussels and king prawns, until I couldn't stand the sight of another shellfish. It was like I was shaking my fist at the Almighty and saying: 'I quit, Your laws are no longer my laws; if You've got something against prawns, OK, but leave me out of it. I'm heading into the sophisticated world where they devour entire clam beds without batting an eyelid. I am no longer one of the prematurely afflicted, I'm shaking off the odour of the voluntary ghetto, I'm heading into the world of prawns. Monte Carlo, Las Vegas, Hollywood, the Italian Riviera; if You're looking for me, that's where You'll find me.' That was more or less my regular harangue against the Almighty.

The week I was on that prawn diet, someone from the Maastricht Theatre School called to say that I hadn't been accepted, and that there was no real reason for me to apply again. I wasn't home, so my father took the call. I had my whole life ahead of me, and there was nothing to do about it.

From *Norwegian Wood*
by Haruki Murakami

Translated from Japanese by JAY RUBIN
The Harvill Press

When the Beatles' song 'Norwegian Wood' plays over the loudspeakers as his plane touches down in Hamburg one day, Taru Watanbe is transported back twenty years to his student life in late 60s Tokyo, and in particular to memories of his childhood friend, Naoko, with whom he is besotted. *Norwegian Wood*, published in two small boxed volumes, one red, one green, achieved cult status in Japan on publication, turning Murakami, already its leading novelist, into a national celebrity. Our extract is taken from the beginning of the 'red' section, as the story opens.

Eighteen years have gone by, and still I can bring back every detail of that day in the meadow. Washed clean of summer's dust by days of gentle rain, the mountains wore a deep, brilliant green. The October breeze set white fronds of head-high grasses swaying. One long streak of cloud hung pasted across a dome of frozen blue. It almost hurt to look at that far-off sky. A puff of wind swept across the meadow and through her hair before it slipped into the woods to rustle branches and send back snatches of distant barking – a hazy sound that seemed to reach us from the doorway to another world. We heard no other sounds. We met no other people. We saw only two bright red birds leap startled from the centre of the meadow and dart into the woods. As we ambled along, Naoko spoke to me of wells.

Memory is a funny thing. When I was in the scene I hardly paid it any attention. I never stopped to think of it as something that would make a lasting impression, certainly never imagined that eighteen years later I would recall it in such detail. I didn't give a damn about the scenery that day. I was thinking about myself. I was thinking about the beautiful girl walking next to me. I was thinking about the two of us together, and then about myself again. I was at that age, that time of life when every sight, every feeling, every thought came back, like a boomerang, to me. And worse, I was in love. Love with complications. Scenery was the last thing on my mind...

...'It's really, *really* deep', said Naoko, choosing her words with care. She would speak that way sometimes, slowing down to find the exact word she was looking for. 'But no one knows where it is,' she continued. 'The one thing I know for sure is that it's around here somewhere.'

Hands thrust into the pockets of her tweed jacket, she smiled at me as if to say 'It's true!'

'Then it must be incredibly dangerous,' I said. 'A deep well, but nobody knows where it is. You could fall in and that'd be the end of you.'

'The end. Aaaaaaaah! Splat! Finished.'

'Things like that must happen.'

'They do, every once in a while. Maybe once in two or three years. Somebody disappears all of a sudden, and they just can't find him. So then the people around here say, "Oh, he fell in the field well".'

'Not a nice way to die,' I said.

'No, it's a terrible way to die,' said Naoko, brushing a cluster of grass seed from her jacket. 'The best thing would be to break your neck, but you'd probably just break your leg and then you couldn't do a thing. You'd yell at the top of your lungs, but nobody would hear you, and you couldn't expect anyone to find you, and you'd have centipedes and spiders crawling all over you, and the bones of the ones who died before are scattered all around you, and it's dark and soggy, and high overhead there's this tiny, tiny circle of light like a winter moon. You die there in this place, little by little, all by yourself.'

'Yuck, just thinking about it makes my flesh creep,' I said. 'Somebody should find the thing and build a wall around it.'

'But nobody *can* find it. So make sure you don't go off the path.'

'Don't worry, I won't.'

Naoko took her left hand from her pocket and squeezed my hand. 'Don't you worry,' she said. 'You'll be OK. *You* could go running all around here in the middle of the night and *you'd* never fall into the well. And as long as I stick with you, I won't fall in, either.'

'Never?'

'Never!'

'How can you be so sure?'

'I just know,' she said, increasing her grip on my hand and walking along in silence. 'I know these things. I'm always right. It's got nothing to do with logic: I just feel it. For example, when I'm really close to you like this, I'm not the least bit scared. Nothing dark or evil could ever tempt me.'

'Well, that's the answer.' I said. 'All you have to do is stay with me like this all the time.'

'Do you mean that?'

'Of course.'

Naoko stopped short. So did I. She put her hands on my shoulders and peered into my eyes. Deep within her own pupils a heavy black liquid swirled in a strange whirlpool pattern. Those beautiful eyes of hers were looking inside me for a long, long time. Then she stretched to her full height and touched her cheek to mine. It was a marvellous, warm gesture that stopped my heart for a moment.

'Thank you.'

'My pleasure,' I answered.

'A Memory of Childhood'
from *The Eyes: A version of Antonio Machado*
by Don Paterson

Faber & Faber

Don Paterson's *The Eyes* is a spiritual portrait of the great Spanish poet Antonio Machado (1873–1939), which lies somewhere between translation and imitation.

A Memory of Childhood

A winter afternoon. The sun
has gone in, and the class begun.
The students settle. Steady rain
lacerates the windowpane.

Dying bells; overhead
a faded poster showing Cain
fugitive, and Abel dead;
by his side, a crimson stain.

A scarecrow in a tattered cloak,
the ancient master slowly stands,
clears his throat, then starts to croak
from the rule-book in his hand.

The children rise at his command
then intone the dismal lesson:
A hundred hundreds make ten thousand.
A thousand thousands make a million.

A winter afternoon. The sun
has gone in, and the class begun.
The students study. Steady rain
lacerates the windowpane.

ALL IN A DAY'S WORK

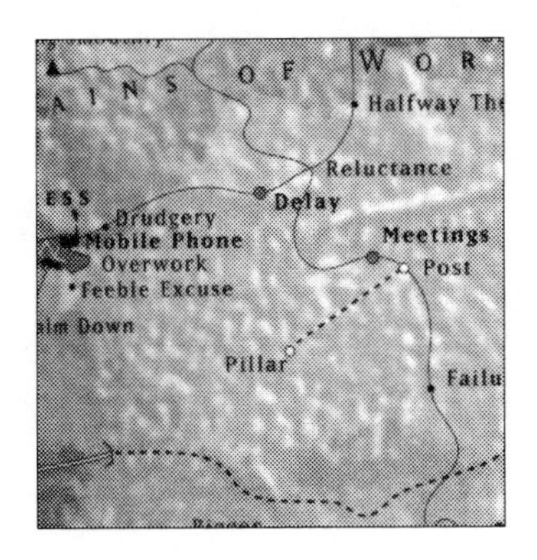

From *The Missing Head of Damasceno Monteiro*
by Antonio Tabucchi,

Translated from Italian by J.C. PATRICK
The Harvill Press

Antonio Tabucchi's *The Missing Head of Damasceno Monteiro* is a crime novel with a difference. Written by an Italian, set in Portugal, the novel explores not only social issues such as racial prejudice and police corruption, but also the metaphysical nature of crime – and death – itself. In this extract, narrator and hero Firmino, a young tabloid journalist has been sent reluctantly to Oporto to investigate the sensational discovery of a headless corpse. One evening at his lodgings, Dona Rosa's pension, he hears of another alarming discovery…

Firmino went to his room. He fell into a lovely sleep as he had hoped to and dreamt about a beach in Madeira, a blue blue sea, and his fiancée. When he woke it was time for dinner, so he put on a jacket and went downstairs. He was lucky enough to find that dinner that evening was a favourite childhood dish, fried hake. He ate ravenously, waited on hand and foot by the young waitress, a hefty lass with a pronounced moustache. The Italian at the next table tried to start a conversation about cuisine, and described a dish of sweet peppers and anchovies which he said came from Piedmont. Firmino courteously pretended to be interested. At that moment Dona Rosa approached him and bent down to whisper in his ear.

'The head has been found,' she said sweetly.

Firmino was looking at the heads of the hake which were left on his plate.

'Head,' he asked like an idiot, 'what head?'

'The head missing from the corpse,' said Dona Rosa amiably 'but there's no hurry, first finish eating your dinner, then I'll tell you all about it and what to do. I'll expect you in the lounge.'

Firmino was unable to restrain his impatience and rushed after her.

'It was found by Senhor Diocleciano,' said Dona Rosa calmly, 'he fished it out of the Douro, so now sit down and listen carefully, come and sit by me.'

And she gave two little taps on the sofa as usual, as if inviting him to have a cup of tea.

'My friend Diocleciano is eighty years old,' Dona Rosa went on, 'he's been a pedlar, a boatman, and he is a fisherman of corpses and suicides in the Douro. Rumour has it that in his life he has fished over seven hundred bodies out of the river. He hands the bodies over to the morgue and the morgue pays him a wage. It's his job. However, this case he knew about in advance, so he has not yet turned the head over to the authorities. He is also the guardian of souls in the Arco dal Alminhas, in the sense that he concerns himself not simply with bodies but also their eternal repose, he lights candles in that holy place, says prayers for them and so on. He has the head at home, he pulled it out of the river a couple of hours ago and let me know, here's his address. But on your way back don't forget to call in at the Alco dal Alminhas and say a prayer for the dead. Meanwhile don't forget to take your camera, before the head ends up in the morgue.'

Firmino went up to his room, fetched his camera and went out in search of a taxi, giving no thought to the carpings of an envious colleague who wrote in his paper that the staff of *Acontecimento* took too many taxis. The ride was brief through the narrow streets of the old city. Senhor Diocleciano lived in a house with a crumbling entrance-way. The door was opened by a plump elderly woman.

'Diocleciano is expecting you in the living-room,' she said, leading the way.

Diocleciano's family living-room was a spacious apartment lit by a chandelier. The furniture, evidently bought at some hypermarket, was fake antique, with gilded legs and tops covered with sheets of glass. On the table in the middle of the room was a head on a dish, as in the Bible story. Firmino gave it a brief nauseated glance and turned to Senhor Diocleciano, who was seated at the head of the table as if playing host at a formal dinner.

'I fished it up at the mouth of the Douro,' he told Firmino. 'I had hooks out for chub and a small net for shrimp, and it got stuck on the hooks.'

Firmino looked at the head on its dish, trying to overcome his repugnance. It must have been in the river some days. It was swollen and purple, one eye had been eaten by fish. He tried to give it an age, but failed. It might have been twenty, but the man could even have been forty.

'I have to turn it in at the morgue,' said Senhor Diocleciano calmly as if it were the most natural thing in the world, 'so if you want to take pictures of it make it quick, because I found it at five o'clock and there's a limit to how much I can lie.'

Firmino took out his camera and clicked away. He photographed the head full face and in profile.

'Have you noticed this?' asked Senhor Diocleciano, 'come closer.'

Firmino did not move. The old man was pointing a finger at one temple.

'Take a look at that.'

Firmino at last brought himself to approach, and saw the hole.

'It's a hole,' he said.

'A bullet hole,' specified Senhor Diocleciano.

Firmino asked Senhor Diocleciano if he might make a telephone call, it would be a short one. He was taken to the telephone in the hall. At the office he got the answering service. Firmino left a message for the Editor.

'Firmino here, the severed head has been found in the river by a fisherman of corpses. I have photographed it. It has a bullet hole in the left temple. I'll send the photos at once by fax or somehow, I'll call by the Luso Agency, perhaps we can bring out a special edition, I'm not thinking of writing anything for the moment, comments are superfluous, I'll be in touch tomorrow.'

He went out into the warm Oporto night. This time he had no desire whatever for a taxi, a good walk was what he needed. But not down to the river, even though it was close by. He had no wish even to look at the river that evening.

'Farmhand'

from *Cusan Dyn Dall/Blind Man's Kiss* by Menna Elfyn

Translated from the Welsh by Elin ap Hywel
Bloodaxe Books

Menna Elfyn's *Cusan Dyn Dall/Blind Man's Kiss*, a bilingual Welsh/English poetry collection, explores Welsh identity with both passion and realism, although its themes are universal. Here she turns her attention to the life of the agricultural worker in rural areas.

Farmhand

He was nothing more
– nor less, for that matter –
than a farmhand in a world of green
driving cows to the dairy
feeding calves and hens,
separating feuding chickens –
small things, part of living, part of death.

What was there here
for any creature, beyond the instinct to survive?
Instinct won out, the night
his father died, the lad
too young to share the grown-ups talk
of a small farmer on a broader acre,
the world beyond – too far away
for well-chosen words in the glacial parlour.
After all, there was milking to do,
another will to be done
and though a boy, the farmhand
knew how to work like a man.

Sometimes when I look
at the far fields of Carmarthenshire
I think of that farmhand.

And ask myself, did something else
die on the farm that day,
was another loss laid to rest?
And in the dairy's long loneliness,
the daily beestings, did
the green acres, overnight
drift into fenceless fields of sleep?

From *De Sade's Valet*
by Nikolaj Frobenius

Translated from Norwegian by TOM GEDDES
Marion Boyars Publishers

A raw and sometimes gut-wrenching evocation of eighteenth-century France – if written by a Norwegian – *De Sade's Valet* takes the bare historical facts surrounding the Marquis de Sade and his real-life valet Georges Latour and transforms them into flesh and bones. A native of Honfleur, Latour is born without the capacity to feel pain. After the death of his mother, he arrives in Paris, determined to find and punish the list of eight men he believes responsible, including his new master, the Marquis de Sade. In the meantime, however, as this extract shows, he remains a loyal servant, even when de Sade is imprisoned.

...Latour is a naïve scientist and one of the major problems in finding a tone for the translation was to reflect this simplicity while avoiding a descent into the banal, a problem compounded by the richness of English vocabulary which could make an over-literal rendering from Norwegian sound too simplistic and repetitive. Latour should come over to the reader not as an evil person, nor as a self-indulgent hedonist, but as a man without empathy because of his inability to feel pain, struggling to understand in order to become the full human being he senses he is not...

Tom Geddes on translating
De Sade's Valet

My master was ranting and raving still, exploding at the slightest little thing. He complained repeatedly about De Launay, the commandant, writing long letters of protest to the Sardinian government and ridiculing the prison warders for their 'supreme stupidity'. I tried to cheer him up with stories of escapes, but it was impossible to improve his mood.

All the way along the route of his exercise walks round the keep, past the curtain walls and the underground cell from which the moaning of a crazed prisoner could be heard, down the path to the kitchen garden and on past the chapel in the lower tower, across the courtyard and back to the cell, all through this daily exercise the Marquis would curse 'the criminal imbeciles who are keeping me locked up'.

He would spit and cough in bitter resentment. 'They're more contemptible than the fish merchants of Aix foisting off their rotten tuna. They're the lackeys of torturers. Madame de Montreuil's bile is spewed over me even down here, Latour, letters of such unfathomable inanity and malice that you would think I had never cared for Renée and my children, never been a devoted son who loved his parents. Am I a monster just because I have amused myself with a few women of the street? Do I not deserve to live?'

I put my hand on his arm – in prison we were of equal worth, or equal worthlessness, and said, 'You are the best man France has.'

Twice a week I went down to Chambéry to fetch the Marquis whatever he might desire: eau de Cologne, orange-blossom water, vanilla bonbons, paper and ink, brandy, candles, medicaments. I did not enjoy these trips out into freedom. I spoke to people as little as possible, tried not to see them as bodies. I wanted to be back inside the castle; I liked the prison life.

No matter how much I brought him, my master was still dissatisfied. Looking at him for signs of optimism, I saw nothing. His whining continued. He suffered headaches, chest pains and an abscess and constantly had to have new medicines.

He talked incessantly, over-stimulating himself, bursting with explanations, anecdotes, ideas. He spoke of God's evil, of nature's 'malevolent molecules' and of his own immorality as if it had been inherent in him since birth. He tried to excuse himself with rational arguments – for a crime he had not committed. I feared he was living in the shadow of his reputation.

I lay dreaming of a world of stone, of what awaited me in Paris: the bodies of numbers five, six and seven. Body number eight was lying breathing beside me here. But I tried not to think about that.

His face was contorted in pain. Was pain a piece of theatre, or was it real? The Marquis had always made a game of pain. At night we would talk about brothels and young female bodies. He spoke of the cruelty of women and maintained that society would be a better place if women whipped their husbands more often. It would spare us from women spreading their venom in other ways. He talked about pain, this resentful nobleman lay on a prison bed fantasizing about tyranny, about the pleasure he found in the physical suffering of others. His constant burbling made me feel ill.

I would fall asleep to the sound of his voice.

I would lie dreaming in a world of stone.

One morning I awoke to hear his groaning. I turned in my bed and found his broad face right up against mine. He was suffering; I could see his grimaces even in the dark, like a language of his own, a language only I understood.

Another morning an Italian made an attempt to escape. He got half way over the second wall before the guards caught him. The prisoners stood at their windows and heard him screaming as he was dragged off. After that there was silence in Miolans.

A few weeks later we were making plans with the Baron de l'Allée, a notorious swindler and former escaper.

The Marquis had asked the commandant if he could take his meals in the lower tower nearer the kitchen, since the food was often cold by the time it reached his table, and the Marquis made it clear that he found it totally unacceptable to have to eat cold food. The commandant had orders to allow him certain privileges and so granted his request. Next to the room in which we were now to eat was the cook's storeroom. Baron de l'Allée had been in to investigate and discovered that it had a window without a grille, the only one in the whole fortress. He thought it was big enough to climb through. Five metres below lay freedom.

The room was kept locked, but the cook had a key.

I went to the kitchen to fetch the midday meal for the Baron and the Marquis. As I poured the soup into bowls and put the chicken on their plates, arranged the marinated artichokes and filled the wine carafe, I thought again of Paris and what awaited me there, numbers five, six and seven. And number eight. But it made me feel dizzy to think too much.

The cook, a short, fat man, had just gone to the dining room, and I knew he would be back in the kitchen in two minutes. He would kick open the door and come rushing in. So I took up position by the door, holding my tray at arms' length, and listened for the sound of his footsteps. Along he came, humming a tune, kicked the door open, and chicken and artichokes flew across the floor, the wine soaked my jacket, the cook cursed and shouted and got down on the floor to pick up the food and put it back on the plates, while I apologized profusely, bent over him and managed to extract the key from his pocket. He spun round and lashed out at me.

'What the hell do you think you're doing?'

I winked at him, whereupon he pushed me away without noticing that his keys were missing. I went back to the Marquis' cell, lit a candle and put a letter from the Marquis on the table. It warned the commandant against trying to recapture us: his private army, the Marquis had written, was waiting for us. Then I returned to the lower tower, served the meal, and we stuffed ourselves with chicken, gulped down the soup and wine and unlocked the door to the storeroom. With the aid of a rope provided by the Baron we let ourselves down into the moat, swam to the other side and sped off through the forest towards the French border.

We ran for several hours and when we reached the border we ran on for yet another hour before we stopped. The Marquis and the Baron lay concealed in the bushes and slept while I kept watch. Through the foliage I could see the Marquis' head and I could hear the Baron snoring. I was trembling with cold and fatigue and kept my feet tucked under me. My face was caked in dried sweat. I sat staring at the Marquis' head. Every time I tried to get up and go over to him I felt sick. It was quite incomprehensible. I sat there the whole night without moving. When dawn broke I came to the conclusion that it was foreordained: I would never be able to bring myself to kill the Marquis.

From *The Twins*
by Tessa de Loo

Translated from Dutch by RUTH LEVITT
Arcadia

The Twins, a million-copy best-seller, tells the story of two sisters, born in 1916 and separated in childhood by the death of their parents and then later by the outbreak of the Second World War. One, Anna, stays in Germany with their grandfather while the other, Lotte, ends up living with an uncle in the Netherlands. When they meet up again after many years, Lotte, who sheltered Jews during the war, is initially suspicious of her new-found sister. But Anna has her own painful tales to tell of wartime hardship. In this extract, while her fiancé, Martin, is fighting on the Russian Front, Anna is keeping house for her aristocratic employers at their dilapidated country estate in Brandenburg – with the help of forced labour.

Thus the renovations began. For a year Anna went from room to room with a succession of Polish labourers and cleaning women from the village until all forty-five had undergone a transformation. The German tenants – sent off to war – had been replaced by Polish forced labourers and Russian prisoners of war, housed in the stables, permanently guarded by four armed soldiers. There were no tractors or petrol. At six o'clock in the morning eighty oxen teams manned by Russians, supervized by an agricultural inspector exempted from military service, went into the surrounding fields with rattling carts, where they worked the whole day at an unRussian pace to fetch in the quota of grain decreed by the Reich. Potatoes, grain, milk, butter, everything had to be handed over, apart from a small ration for individual use. For the castle inhabitants a wall cupboard had been constructed with compartments in which each kept their own store of butter – one hundred and twenty-five grams per week. They had to hand over half to the kitchen for cooking, the other half was for bread. Humanity seemed to be divided into two camps: the one spread everything on one piece and had dry bread for the rest of the week, the other carefully spread each piece with a puritanically wafer-thin layer…

…After the sugar beets had been harvested they were washed, sliced and pressed in a nauseatingly sweet smoke by the Polish women. Then they were made into a syrup; everything was sticky and clinging. Each one got a sack of beets for themselves as payment. 'May we use the press…?' they gestured, shyly demonstrating how hard pressing by hand in a cloth was. 'Of course,' said Anna, 'we've finished, we don't need it any more.' Some hours later Herr von Garlitz came up to her in riding attire. 'Listen here,' he called her to order, 'now what have you done? You have given the Poles the press.' 'Yes, why not?' said Anna defiantly. She was irritated by the fashionable, indolent element in the middle of the hum of activity. 'Do you think,' he raised his chin, 'the Poles would give us a press if we were in Poland?' He looked challengingly at her and answered for her:

'They certainly would not do so, precisely because they hate us.' 'But after all, we don't hate them,' Anna retorted, 'anyway, if the Poles are so much worse than us, as you say, and I am meant to follow their example and be like them, then that makes us not a whisker better and we have no right to behave as though they ought to obey us.' He shook his head at the paradoxical reasoning. 'They are Untermenschen,' he said with dignity. 'If they are Untermenschen and we are the Herrenmenschen, as you say, she tried to put it diplomatically, 'then actually I can't be like the Poles, so shouldn't I be like us, namely a Herrenmensch!' The whole idea of Untermensch, Herrenmensch, Übermensch struck her as ridiculous, but she had just enough political awareness to understand intuitively that she could not say that out loud to a lackey of the Fuhrer. Von Garlitz frowned; this dialectic was going, over his head. Somewhere he sensed he had been put in his place by a self-opinionated, unfortunately indispensable, member of the staff who impudently deployed her power against his, as employer, over his household. It was all too much for him; shaking the confusion off him he walked away with short, measured steps, his head bent, thwacking a tree here and there with his riding whip...

...One of the Russian prisoners carried unusual responsibilities: he had to light the stoves in the castle and keep them going. Day in, day out, he went from room to room with a basket of wood. No one said anything to him – it was punishable to regard Russians as human beings. One day Anna found herself in a room with him. Shy, almost invisible, he did his work as though he had realized that he had no right to exist except as the bringer of fire. She spoke to him, without preliminaries, simply because they were two individuals in one space. To her surprise, he replied in broken German – moreover he appeared to be called Wilhelm: after the German Kaiser had visited the Tsar, all new-born babies had been called Wilhelm. Another godchild of the emperor, Anna grinned to herself. His explanation was full of softly vibrating Russian consonants. After the first introduction, she could regularly be found in rooms where the stove was being lit. They were suffering from hunger in the stables, he whispered, there were shortages of everything.

She stole food for him from the kitchen. In the evenings she cut discarded blue checked quilt covers into pieces and made them into handkerchiefs for the prisoners. She collected discarded toothbrushes, remains of toothpaste, pocket combs with a few broken teeth and soap. Wilhelm smuggled the spoils to the stables where they were eagerly put to use. She did not ask herself why she did it; subversive intentions were strange to her – she simply could not tolerate the disharmony between the relative comfort in the castle and the hardship in the stables.

The Adversary: A True Story of Murder and Deception
by Emmanuel Carrère

Translated from French by LINDA COVERDALE
Bloomsbury

One January morning in 1993 Jean-Claude Romand shot dead his wife, his parents and his two children before setting fire to his family home in the Jura region of France. A major best-seller, *The Adversary* chillingly uncovers the real-life story behind a horrific murder case, detailing Carrère's own correspondence and dealings with Romand himself, a man who had been living a lie for most of his adult life; for rather than the distinguished health official with a senior position at the World Health Organisation in Geneva he'd always claimed to be, Romand had no formal medical qualifications and in fact didn't work at all...

In the mornings, he was the one who drove the children to the Ecole Saint-Vincent. He would accompany them into the courtyard, exchange a few words with the teachers or the students' mothers (who held up as an example to their husbands this father who was so close to his children), then drive off towards Geneva. It's a little over a mile to the border, crossed twice a day by the several thousand residents of the Gex region who work in Switzerland. Like commuters on a suburban train, they have regular schedules; they greet one another and the customs officers who wave them through without inspection. Many are international civil servants and when they enter the city, instead of turning right towards the business district and the Cornavin railway station, go left towards the botanical garden and the residential neighbourhood where their organizations have their headquarters. Romand joined this stream of traffic, cruising along the wide and placid green avenues, more often than not ending up in the carpark of WHO. Entering with a visitor's badge, carrying a briefcase, he followed a familiar orbit, going from the ground-floor library to the conference rooms and the publications office, where he systematically swept up anything printed and free: his house and car overflowed with papers bearing the letterhead or stamp of WHO. He used all the services offered by the organization – a post office where he sent his mail, a bank where he made most of his withdrawals, a travel agency through which he planned the family holidays – but did not risk going upstairs, where security guards might have asked him what he was looking for. Did he at least once, taking advantage of momentarily deserted halls, visit the office with the window marked by an X on the photo of the building he'd given his parents? Did he look outside, his forehead pressed against the glass, at what there was to see from that window? Did he sit in *his* chair, did he walk by the fellow coming back to sit there, did he call him on his direct line? He says no, the thought never even crossed his mind. His mother-in-law remembers that one Sunday when the whole family had gone to Switzerland, the children had wanted to see Papa's office, so Papa had agreed to the detour. They'd pulled into the carpark, he'd pointed out the window. And that's all.

In the beginning he went to WHO every day, later on less regularly. Instead of the road to Geneva, he'd take the one to Gex and Divonne or the one to Bellegarde that leads to the motorway and Lyon. He'd stop at a newsstand to buy an armful of papers: dailies, magazines, scientific journals. Then he'd go and read them, either in a café – he was careful to change cafés often and to choose them far enough from home – or in his car. He would park in a carpark or at a service station and stay there for hours, reading, taking notes, dozing. He'd have a sandwich for lunch and continue reading throughout the afternoon in a different café, at a different service station. When this routine became too monotonous, he'd stroll around Bourg-en-Bresse, Bellegarde, Gex, Nantua, and especially Lyon, where he visited his favourite bookshops, FNAC and Flammarion on the Place Bellecour. Other days, he needed open air and nature and would drive into the Jura Mountains. He followed the winding road that leads to the pass of La Faucille, where there is an inn called the Wood Grouse. Florence and the children liked to go there on Sundays to ski and eat chips. During the week it was deserted. He'd have a glass of wine, go walking in the forest. From the crest of the mountain one can see the countryside around Gex, Lake Geneva and, on a clear day, the Alps. Spread out before him was the civilized plain where Dr Romand and others like him lived; behind him were the narrow valleys and dark forests where he'd spent his lonely childhood. On Thursdays, when he taught a course in Dijon, he would visit his parents, who were delighted to show off to their neighbours this great big son who was so important, so busy, but always ready to go out of his way to give them a hug and a kiss...

...Lastly, there were the trips – conferences, seminars, symposiums, all over the world. He would buy a guide to the country; Florence would pack his suitcase. He'd drive off in his car, which he would supposedly leave in the long-term carpark at Geneva airport. In a comfortable hotel room, often near the airport, he would take off his shoes, stretch out on the bed, spend three or four days watching television and the planes taking off and landing outside his window. He studied the guidebooks so he wouldn't make any mistakes in his stories when he got home. He telephoned his family every day to tell them what time it was and what the weather was like in São Paulo or Tokyo. He'd ask how things were going in his absence. He'd tell his wife, his children, his parents that he missed them, was thinking of them, sent them a big kiss. He phoned no one else: whom would he have called? After a few days, he went home with presents bought in an airport gift shop. Everyone made a fuss over him. He was tired from jet lag.

MARRIAGE AND FAMILY LIFE

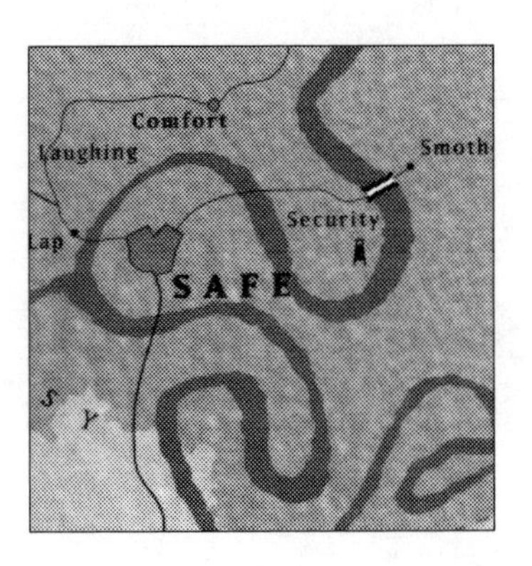

From *The Alphonse Courrier Affair*
by Marta Morazzoni

Translated from Italian by EMMA ROSE
The Harvill Press

The Alphonse Courrier Affair, which won the 2001 *Independent* Foreign Fiction Prize, is set in a tiny Auvergne village in the late nineteenth and early twentieth centuries. Here, the novel's eponymous hero, a prosperous ironmonger, lives out his seemingly perfect life, with a beautiful but cool wife, two young sons and a secret mistress until events slowly conspire to overwhelm him. In this extract he views his own marriage ceremony with typical detachment.

...he was now sitting on a kind of diminutive red velvet throne, his future wife at his side. Future? For a moment he felt disorientated. Did 'future' mean in five minutes' time? He stole a glance at the watch he kept in the pocket of the waistcoat he was wearing for the occasion – heavy material at the front and pearl-grey satin at the back. It suited him; the neatness of the trimmings allowed it to be worn without a jacket when necessary. There were less than five minutes to go. They seemed to have drawn very close to the event while his thoughts were wandering around the nave. The girl at his side probably had more of a grip on the situation: she, most likely, had been paying attention. Courrier pulled himself together; he had been in danger of weighing anchor too early.

And, sure enough, at that moment the rings appeared. It still wasn't quite time, however. From an unseen corner of the church, some functionary had dispatched two children, bearing the gold circles on a small cushion, and now they stood behind the protagonists, ready to pounce. They were in fancy dress too, poor little creatures. Even the children. The offspring of man, they suffered the consequences of sartorial vanity as soon as they had use of their legs...The small couple saw themselves reflected in the adult one. Courrier found it easy to reward them both with a sincere smile when they held out the red cushion with its golden rings.

Rings which, shortly afterwards, were sparkling on the fingers of man and wife. The childish couple had separated, returning to the anonymity of the pews, and an indelible adult couple had been formed. It had taken no more than a moment. A brief formula, barely audible from the front rows (the girl half-way down the nave certainly wouldn't have heard a thing) and Alphonse Courrier ceased to be alone in the world. All calculated to perfection – yet, for a fraction of a second, he felt giddy. The possibility of that something – that crazed variable – skewing the rules of the game and wrong-footing its players flashed through his mind. He turned in fear to the stranger at his side and saw her smile calmly, her expression barely veiled by a hint of emotion. He was gripped by the suspicion that this woman, Agnès Duval, might be even more calculating than he was. A woman's coldness can far exceed a man's rationality, since it is born of a deeper knowledge of life. Totally lacking in theory, it heeds only concrete results.

She was still smiling. Courrier noticed that his bride's gums grew low over her teeth, so that her smile uncovered an area of pink which he had never noticed before. He responded with a tight-lipped smile. Peasant culture, sober and reserved, did not allow for the newlyweds to kiss on the mouth, which was just as well. The guests saw to it that the bride's cheeks were covered in kisses as soon as she left the church. For his part, Courrier received embraces, handshakes, and the odd salacious remark, which he accepted with the cheerful composure of a man who had already crossed certain thresholds.

Courrier did not find the reception too wearying, even though it went on till late. As for afterwards, he slept as easily as he had on the previous night. Perhaps even better: in the first place because he really was tired, and secondly because the step he had taken filled him with the quiet satisfaction which comes with completing one leg of a journey. The following day was a Sunday; the shop would remain shut; his life was beginning in the most auspicious of ways. Another reason for sleeping soundly could have been the carrying our of his conjugal duties, but why fulfil them according to the standards and expectations of others? The village had sought to solemnize this copulation, and the village had been satisfied. As for Courrier, he had his whole life ahead of him, and slept the more soundly for it. The next morning Agnès Duval was still Agnès Duval – Madame Courrier only in the eyes of Mother Church and the Town Hall.

From *The Same Sea*
by Amos Oz

Translated from Hebrew by NICHOLAS DE LANGE with the author
Chatto & Windus

In a series of short, lyrical chapters, many more like poems than prose, Amos Oz's most recent novel, *The Same Sea*, charts the progress of a group of friends and family following the death of Nadia Danon from cancer. Here, Nadia's first, unhappy marriage is described.

Butterflies to a Tortoise

At sixteen and a half, in a country town, she was married to a
well-off relative.
A widower aged thirty. It was the custom
to marry daughters within the family. Her father
was a gold and silversmith. One of the brothers was sent to Sofia,
to study to be a pharmacist and bring back a diploma. Nadia
herself learned from her mother how to cook and embroider,
make sweetmeats and write neatly. The widowed bridegroom, a
draper,
came to visit on Sabbaths and holidays. If asked, he sang
wonderfully in a rich, resonant tenor voice. He was a tall, elegant,
well-mannered
man,
who always knew what to say
and what to pass over in silence. Nadia's heart
was not in the marriage, because her best friend whispered to her
what love was really like: it must not be stirred until it pleases.

But her parents, patiently, understandingly, brought her to another
point
of view. Surely to do her duty was also in her own best interest. And
they set
a date, not too soon; they wanted to give her enough time
to become accustomed gradually to the widower, who never failed
to bring her a present. Sabbath by Sabbath
she learned to like the sound of his voice. Which was pleasant.

After the wedding her husband turned out to be a considerate man
who inclined to a measure of regularity in intimate matters. Every
evening,
scrubbed, scented and cheerful, he would come and sit on the edge
of the bed. He started with a gentle word of affection, turned out
the light
to spare her blushes, drew aside the sheet, caressed her sparingly,

and eventually rested his hand on her breast. She was always
on her back, her nightdress rolled up, he was always on top of her,
while outside the door the pendulum wall-clock with gilt fittings
slowly beat time. He rammed. He groaned. Had she wished, every
night
she could have counted about twenty moderate thrusts, the final one
reinforced with a tenor note. Then he wrapped himself up and slept.
In the thick darkness she lay empty; and bewildered
for another hour at least. Sometimes solacing her body herself. In a
whisper
she told her closest friend, who would say, When there is love
it feels different, but how can you explain butterflies to a tortoise.

Several times she woke at five, put on a housecoat and went up on
the roof
to fetch in the washing. She could see empty rooftops, a patch of
forest,
a deserted plain. Then her father and her husband, setting off
together
to early-morning prayers. Day after day she shopped and cleaned
and cooked. On Sabbath eves guests came, imbibed and dined
and nibbled and argued. On her back in bed when it was all over
she sometimes had thoughts about a baby.

'Letter To My Wife'
from *Camp Notebook* by Miklós Radnóti

Translated from Hungarian by FRANCIS R. JONES
Arc

An extraordinary and unique collection of poems, Hungarian poet Miklós Radnóti's *Camp Notebook* was written in secret – often on scraps of paper or labels – during his incarceration in Nazi slave-labour camps during the war. After his death, shot on a forced march in 1944, his body was exhumed and the poems found in his pocket. 'Letter To My Wife' was written for Fanni Gyarmati, whom he had married in 1935.

Letter To My Wife

Down in the depths the listening worlds are mute,
the silence screams in my ear and I cry out,
but no-one can reply from Serbia, where
the land has fainted into distance and war,
and you are far away. My dreams have caught
your voice – by day I find it here in my heart –
I'm listening now, the murmur's all round me,
the cool brushing of ferns rising up proudly.

I've no idea when I'll see you once more,
and you who were as solemn as psalms, and sure,
as beautiful as light, as shade – I could find
my way home to you, though I were dumb and blind –
you're hiding in the land, flickering inside
my eyes, projected from within by my mind;
you've become dream again, though you were essence:
falling back into the well of adolescence,

I ask the jealous question – do you love me?
and once, at youth's very summit, will you be
my wife, one day? And once again I hope and,
falling back on the road of life, eyes open,
now I know that you are. My wife, and my friend –
it's only that you're so far away! Beyond
three wild frontiers. Autumn's coming: might it
lose me here? Kisses – their memory's brighter;

I placed my faith in miracles and ignored
the days; when bombers passed above me in hordes,
I admired the blue of your eyes in the sky;
but the sky turned grey, and in the planes, up high,
were bombs longing to fall. Despite them, I live –
and I am captive. All I hope for I have
surveyed, but I still know the way back to you;
I've walked the length and breadth of the soul for you,

and the roads of many lands; if it's my fate
to walk on purple coals through the tumbling flame,
I'll witch myself another shape, and be back
again; if need be, I can be tough as bark
on a tree: in this endless, perilous plight,
a prey for wild men's weapons, their savage might,
a calm calms me, and washes over me now
like a cool wave: the saneness of 2 x 2.

Lager Heidenau,
in the hills above Zagubica, VIII–LIX 1944

From *Losing Eugenio*
by Geneviève Brisac

Translated from French by J.A. UNDERWOOD
Marion Boyars Publishers

Losing Eugenio, a huge success in France, selling over 150,000 copies and winning the Prix Femina, details the gradual mental disintegration of Nouk, formerly an artist and now a full-time single mother, as she tries to care for her son Eugenio in Paris. The book opens at Christmas as Nouk attempts to reassure Eugenio – and herself – that all will be well.

As we climbed the stairs, me in front and him behind, clinging to my skirts, a hangover from the time (not all that long ago) when I used to carry him up, in defiance of every recommendation, cocking a snook at the entire medical profession, through sheer stupidity, I remembered what he'd been saying a moment before: 'Get your skates on mummy, we're late.'

'Who are we late for?' I asked suspiciously, and he laughed.

'That was just a trick to make you go faster,' he muttered, a little unnerved by his own insolence. 'You're always saying there's no education but by example. "We're late" are the two words you say most often.' He mimicked the face I make, neck tensed, jaws clenched, brow furrowed with anxiety: '"We're late, hurry up darling!"'

'But I don't do that when it's holidays!'

'I do,' Eugenio answered. 'Look, it's nearly Christmas, mummy. We really do have to get our skates on. Where are we going, anyway, we're not staying here, are we, getting on each other's nerves? Other people have families they love, what's to become of us?'

'While we're on the subject, what are we going to eat?' I asked.

A clear voice from the depths of the sofa suggested: 'McDonald's?'

'A McDonald's that I go out and fetch you, or a McDonald's that we eat there, like lovers?' My grounded poet hesitated, startled by such indulgence.

'That you go out and fetch,' he concluded after mature reflection. And I felt a pang of anguish. 'All right, love. What kind of McDonald's?'

Before going out again, I drew the curtains that I had eventually put up in our living-room, blood-red, heavy curtains, extremely formal. They reminded me of when I had worked in the theatre, that was what they were there for, to remind me of worlds I had resigned from. I looked down at the narrow street. The dark winter night is different for every window, I mused. In the one-and-a-half rooms where Eugenio and I had been living for two years, there were two. Directly opposite, let into the opposite wall, there was a plaque I had never noticed before, a sort of little scene, green, lit by a tiny spotlight. It seemed to show a landscape, boulders probably, and a lake. It was hard to make out anything but silvery reflections. I was reminded of Ys, the magical Breton city that only comes up out of the water once in a hundred years.

The McDonald's in the boulevard was half-empty. On the left as you came in, just inside the door, sat Violet. That was my name for her, anyway, because she was a woman at peace. Violet would tell me things from time to time, it was why she came there, to have a chat with someone. She would carry over her orange plastic box containing some mess she had concocted herself, using other people's debris. I never asked her what she was eating, we talked about our children, about life. That evening she had finished her meal and was clearing things away, muttering to herself. She picked up about twenty drinking-straws and stuffed them into her large bag, where they joined the empty plastic bags that rustled as she walked. The existence of Violet, far from distressing me, reassured me. Why? Because of her graceful movements, I think, and because she was not sad, despite the fact that she was old, poor and on her own.

Farther down the spacious interior full of orange reflections, half-hidden behind the central pillar, I spotted the thoughtful, happy face of the tramp who used to spend the day begging just up the street. He virtually lived in the restaurant. He slept there, ate there twice a day, always at the same time, using the same table. He was a resident, he would fasten his paper serviette around his neck.

I took the order back up to my son, together with a large fries, Chinese sauce and a straw.

'Put it down at my feet, slave,' he said.

I had not even taken off my coat. I couldn't help the tears that stung my eyes at that moment. I wasn't proud of them either, any more than I was of the smack that then landed on the spiky top of his head. The fries went flying.

'You always spoil things!' I shouted.

'It was just a joke, mummy,' he spluttered. 'You have no sense of humour, you really don't. You're only thinking of yourself when you claim to be thinking of everybody. It doesn't work, and that's why you're on your own, why we're both here, the two of us, like a couple of dead rats.'

I wanted to go over to him, put my hand on his arm. I thought of those mothers whose children hit them, making people mutter: 'Serves them right. You spoil children like that, you turn them into monsters.'

'If you don't spoil them,' another voice whispered, 'you turn them into cripples.'

Eugenio did not hit me, he snuggled up to me. I sensed he was crying. We watched a quiz show: *Saved by the Bell.*

'Don't worry about Christmas,' I murmured to him, 'I've got it all planned, it's a surprise, you'll like it.'

I said this as I turned out the light. I stayed to watch him fall asleep. Never do that, the doctor would tell me every time.

Only dead mothers, I sometimes caught myself thinking, do no harm. They are the kindest ones, the really perfect ones.

The truth is, I watched my son fall asleep for the beauty of that silent moment, that split second when everything tips over. I watched him fall asleep. I took the time, the way I take time out to gaze at flowers. I just did it, trying to understand.

Only two days to Christmas Eve, I jingled in amazement as I fell asleep myself. How shall we get through it this time?

‘Alienation Through Work’
by Karin Kiwus

Translated from German and collected in **Faint Harps and Silver Voices: Selected Translations** by CHRISTOPHER MIDDLETON
Carcanet

Karin Kiwus’ poetry tightly interweaves the private, domestic, intimate sphere of everyday life with larger social issues of feminist politics and identity. Here, in a poem written in 1976, a couple’s simple morning routine reflects the changing dynamic of their relationship.

...Translation is a species of mime, and as the mime embodies another human being, the translator's envoices other voices in his own tonal scale...you go into the text, you tease out of yourself a faculty for hearing the nuances, you catch twisted rays of splendour and untwist them...

Christopher Middleton on translating poetry

Alienation Through Work

To me it really makes no difference
  helping you in the kitchen
    but sometimes now I miss
  these hesitant half-moments
leaning against the doorpost and looking at you
  the way you put a breakfast together
    with your whole body

You always measured out the tea
  pinch by pinch
    in the hollow of your left hand
and with your teeth
  tore a packet of sliced cheese open
the frigidaire door
  you shut with your thigh
and crushed the bulky egg cartons
  with your wooden soled shoes

You always pushed with your elbow
  saucepans off the cooker top
and placed others on it, hardly to be lifted
  with both hands

You always had these pan handles
  in one hand
    and a cookie in the other
and a cloth slipping off your shoulder
  when any liquid spilled on the floor
and you with bare toes
  pulled a floorcloth out and wiped it up
as if a lathe were underneath your foot

And puffcheeked like a sleepy angel
with a slightly distant look
you always blew on the boiling milk
and the five-minute eggs you put
hot into the breast pocket of your bathrobe

It was always such a relief
to notice how with complete confidence
you could take a hold on anything in the mornings
self-oblivious and with an agility
which made me feel at one with you
at first sight

Now when I stand beside you in the kitchen
and in my own way
attentively cope with things
I no longer have my eyes on you
And since we really began to be together
I have stopped feeling deep down
how it really is
when you and I begin a day

I am closer to you perhaps
but you are always
half an hour
ahead of me now

PASSIONATE AFFAIRS

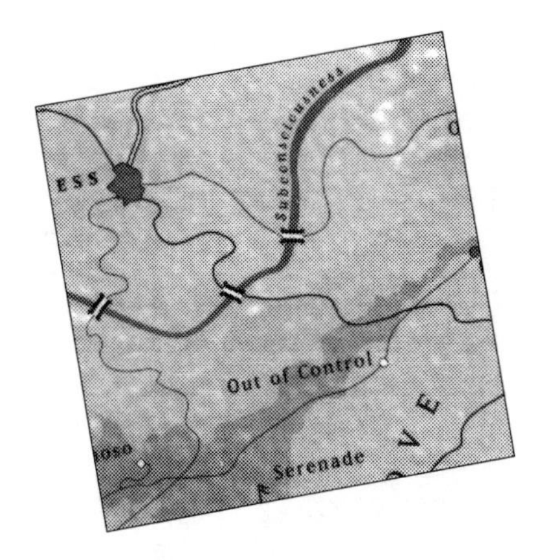

'Song 88'
from *Song Offerings* by Rabindranath Tagore

Translated from Bengali by JOE WINTER
Anvil

Rabindranath Tagore's *Gitanjali* or *Song Offerings* is a series of 150 devotional poems, originally written to be sung. Here, as in so many of the song-prayers, earthly and divine love are ambiguously treated as one.

Song 88

You I want. Only you,
  dearest, I desire.
Let me always say this from
  the heart, no liar.
Other hopes of night and day
that lead me on, lead me astray;
for all are false. Only you,
  dearest, I desire.

As night's prayer-word is unheard
  that seeks sun's fire –
so dream-deluded, it is you,
  dearest, I desire.
As peace is shattered by storm's riot
and yet at heart that storm seeks quiet –
so injuring you, yet only you,
  dearest, I desire.

From *Les Liaisons Culinaires*
by Andreas Staïkos

Translated from Greek by ANNE-MARIE STANTON-IFE
The Harvill Press

In *Les Liaisons Culinaires*, a first novel by Greek playwright Andreas Staïkos, Dimitris and Damocles, two neighbours in an Athenian block of flats, have discovered that they are both having an affair with the same women, the married Nana. To gain the upper hand in her affections, both men try to woo her by cooking succulent, delectable dishes, although the results aren't always what they might wish. Here, Dimitris tries his hand…

...Staïkos bases his narrative of intrigue and erotic rivalry around classics of Greek cuisine, ranging from the much maligned moussaka to the traditional Easter offal-based dishes. The quintessentially Greek flavour of the novel derives from these recipes, and thus the challenge it presents to a translator lies not so much in cultural specifics (Staïkos tells us little about the three lovers or their environment) but in maintaining the playfulness of the original, the stylistic range, irony and economy of Staïkos' writing; in short, to foreground the theatrical quality of this playwright's first novel...

Anne-Marie Stanton-Ife on translating *Les Liaisons Culinaires*

Two hours later, Nana was in Dimitris' flat, seated at a sumptuous dinner table, and in the soft candlelight embarked on an extremely faltering explanation of why she had been delayed. She inserted her fork into her mouth at regular intervals, so that each sentence was truncated, irritating Dimitris beyond measure.

'I was about to leave the house,' she said, cutting off this improvisation by conveying a small mouthful of lamb between her cherry-red lips. Once she had swallowed, she resumed her narrative, continuing her delivery in a soft, measured voice, as though giving dictation. 'And just as I was about to leave, almost at the front door, in fact...' Another mouthful – peas this time – stopped her flow.

'Yes, you were just about to leave *and*?' Dimitris demanded, trying to force the conclusion from her.

'Well, I was dressed exactly as I am now.' (Mouthful. Pause.)

'And?'

'Who should turn up out of the blue? My husband, that's who.' Her voice was so faint and her delivery so slow and laboured that she was barely audible.

'Why the hushed voice? I can hardly hear you.'

'Oh, I don't know. It must be the food. So tender, it caresses the mouth like velvet, subduing me to a whisper. I've never tasted more delicious lamb and peas. Bravo, Dimitris! How did you manage to get the sauce this red-gold colour? How did you manage to temper that violent tomato-red, to tame it with shades of burnished yellow?' The words were uttered slowly, in Nana's throaty, velvet tones – and with no hesitation stemming the flow of her praise.

'So your husband turns up quite "out of the blue"? Then what?' Dimitris steered her back to her narrative, more interested in her explanation than her flattery.

'Yes, so, my husband turns up out of the blue,' she repeated, clearly attempting to buy the time to prepare her next lie.

'Yes. Your husband turns up totally out of the blue.' Dimitris was now dangerously close to losing his temper,

'Well, when he appeared, I was taken by surprise.' (Mouthful of lettuce.) 'I wasn't expecting him. He was supposed to be having dinner with some people.' (A smidgen of aubergine salad.)

'With some people?'

'Yes, foreign businessmen.'

'So?' Aggressive now.

'He was a bit surprised to see me dressed up,' she said, and continued her story in a single breath without any assistance from her fork, confident now of the plot. 'He had thought I was staying at home this evening – I had assured him of this as he was leaving the house this morning. I explained that I wasn't dressed up because I was going out but because I had just got back from the hairdresser's. When he said that I looked exactly the same as I had earlier, I told him that there was such a thing as preventative hairdressing, since it is crucial to discipline those awkward, unmanageable wisps and curls, or total anarchy might ensue. He replied that if salons did not come up with a solution to the problems of the female coiffure soon, the entire male population would unite in a deracinating frenzy and deal with the situation once and for all.'

Dimitris began to make inroads into his food, appearing satisfied by Nana's entertaining excuses. In truth, he was rather flattered that she would go to such lengths to concoct these fanciful lies.

'Here's to you!' They drank to her good health.

'From the moment I started growing my nails and wearing a higher heel – in other words, since the day I met you,' Nana continued, unabashed, 'I think my husband has sensed that his manhood is threatened.' She sighed.

'Why the sigh?'

'A bad sign! There may be trouble ahead. Him turning up like that shows how insecure he's feeling. He doesn't trust me. He's watching me. He's trying to corner me. He turns up when I least expect it, and disappears when I *am* expecting him. Do you know, he tried on four suits before he eventually left? He said that the first two clashed with his tie, and changed the second two because his tie clashed with the suits. And you can be sure that he would have gone on to a fifth, a sixth, a seventh had he not seen me take off my clothes, remove my make-up and get into my pyjamas. As soon as he'd left, I did my face again and got back into these clothes. And of course, I'll have to undress again in a minute, and before I leave get dressed again, then go home and get undressed once more. My life has been reduced to an interminable cycle of dressing and undressing, undressing and dressing. But Dimitris: these perfect, little round spheres, these perfect, tender peas, how do you do it?'

'What are we going to do about your husband?'

'Let's forget about him, shall we? I don't come here to think about my husband. I want to know how you get them so perfectly spherical. Sheer magic!'

'But suppose he tries to call you now that he thinks you are at home. What then?' Dimitris was worrying about the future.

'Do you answer the phone when you're asleep?'

'True, but what if he comes home early?'

'Well he won't find me, will he? I'll tell him that I had an excruciating toothache, so I dashed off to the dentist.'

'The dentist? At midnight?'

'Yes. If the pain is unbearable. Anyway, I've complained to him so often about my tooth that he wouldn't be surprised. We must prepare ourselves for every possibility and take necessary precautions. In fact, I'll give him your phone number, and if need be, you'll have to pretend to be my dentist. Mmm, what gorgeous peas. What heavenly spheres!'

'Nana! Shut up about the peas! You are giving me a headache. Peas, peas, peas! What's got into you? You're giving me indigestion! The world is coming to an end, your husband is consumed with jealousy, we are on the brink of catastrophe, and all you can think about is peas! Have mercy! Forget the peas! They'll be the death of me!'

****

Lamb with Peas

Shell ½ kg of peas. Place them in a saucepan of boiling water for 4–5 minutes and drain.

In a large casserole, sauté small pieces of lamb in a generous amount of olive oil until reddish-brown all over. Remove the lamb pieces and drain the oil.

Finely slice 5–6 bulbous spring onions and sauté them in fresh olive oil (a smaller amount than used for the lamb). Add 1 level tablespoon of flour, stirring vigorously with a wooden spoon to prevent lumps forming. Next, add the juice of 2 large, ripe tomatoes and a cup of water.

Season the lamb pieces and place them back in the saucepan. Reduce the heat and simmer for 30 minutes. Finally, add the peas and generous quantities of finely chopped fresh dill, and allow to simmer for a further 30 minutes.

*****

From the short story **'The Red Coral Bracelet'** collected in *The Summerhouse, Later* by Judith Hermann

Translated from German by MARGOT BETTAUER DEMBO
Flamingo

In 'The Red Coral Bracelet', a story from Judith Hermann's acclaimed first collection, *The Summerhouse, Later*, a young German woman attempts to rouse her depressed German-Russian lover with tales of their linked past; of the time her great-grandmother spent alone in St Petersburg, homesick for Germany, while her husband travelled Russia building furnaces, as well as the story of the bracelet itself.

In those years, in addition to foreign businessmen and their families, many Russian artists and scholars lived on Vasilevsky Ostrov. It was inevitable that they would hear of the German woman, the beautiful pale one with the fair hair who was said to live up on Maly Prospekt, almost always by herself and in rooms as dark, soft, and cool as the sea. The artists and scholars went to see her. My great-grandmother gestured with her small weary hand, asking them to come in. She spoke little, she scarcely understood anything they said, slowly and dreamily she gazed at them from under heavy eyelids. The artists and scholars sat down on the deep, soft sofas and chairs, sinking into the heavy, dark materials; the maids brought black cinnamoned tea with huckleberry and blackberry jam. My great-grandmother warmed her cold hands on the samovar and felt much too tired to ask the artists and scholars to leave. And so they stayed. And they looked at my great-grandmother, and in the dusk my great-grandmother merged into something melancholy, beautiful, and foreign. And since melancholy and beauty and foreignness are essential traits of the Russian soul, the artists and scholars fell in love with my great-grandmother, and my great-grandmother let herself be loved by them.

My great-grandfather stayed away for a long time. And so my great-grandmother let herself be loved for a long time – she did it carefully and circumspectly, and she made hardly any mistakes. Warming her cold hands on the samovar and her chilled soul on the ardent hearts of her lovers, she learned to distinguish – in that strange strange, soft language of theirs – the words: 'You are the most tender of all birches.' She read the letters about the smelting furnaces, the Deville furnaces, and the tube furnaces in the narrow chink of daylight and burned them all in the fireplace. She allowed herself to be loved; in the evening before falling asleep she sang the song about the Blome Wildnis, sang it to herself, and when her lovers looked at her inquiringly, she smiled and said nothing.

My great-grandfather promised to come back soon, to go back to Germany with her soon. But he did not come.

The first, the second, and then the third St Petersburg winter passed, and still my great-grandfather was busy building furnaces in the Russian vastness, and still my great-grandmother was waiting for the time when she could return home to Germany. She wrote to him in the taiga. He wrote back that he would return soon but that he would have to leave again one more time, just one last time – but then, but then, he promised, then they could leave.

The evening of his arrival my great-grandmother was sitting in front of the mirror in her bedroom, combing her fair hair. The gifts from her lovers lay in a little jewellery box before the mirror, the brooch from Grigori, the ring from Nikita, the pearls and velvet ribbons from Alexei, the locks of hair from Jemelyan, the medallions, amulets, and silver bracelets from Mikhail and Ilya. The little jewellery box also held the red coral bracelet from Nikolai Sergeyevich. Its six hundred and seventy-five little coral beads were strung onto a silken thread, and they glowed as red as rage. My great-grandmother put the hairbrush down in her lap. She closed her eyes for a long time. Then she opened her eyes again, took the red coral bracelet from the little box and fastened it around her left wrist. Her skin was very white.

That evening, for the first time in three years, she shared a meal with my great-grandfather. My great-grandfather spoke Russian and smiled at my great-grandmother. My great-grandmother folded her hands in her lap and smiled back at him. My great-grandfather talked about the steppe, about the wilderness, about the Russian 'White Nights,' he talked about the furnaces and called them by their German names, and my great-grandmother nodded as though she understood. My great-grandfather said in Russian that he had to go once more to Vladivostok, he was eating pelmeni with his fingers as he said it; he wiped the grease from his lips with his hands, he said that Vladivostok was the last stop, then it would be time to return to Germany. Or would she like to stay longer?

My great-grandmother did not understand what he said. But she understood the word Vladivostok. She placed her hands on the table, and on her left white wrist the coral bracelet glowed red as rage.

My great-grandfather stared at the coral bracelet. He put what was left of his pelmeni back on his plate, wiped his hands on the linen napkin, and gestured to the maid to leave the room. In German he said, 'What's that?'

My great-grandmother said, 'A bracelet.'

My great-grandfather said, 'And where did you get it, if I may ask?'

Very softly and gently my great-grandmother said, 'You may. I wish you had asked me all along. It's a present from Nikolai Sergeyevich.'

My great-grandfather called the maid back and sent her to get his friend Isaak Baruw. Isaak Baruw arrived; he was hunchbacked and stooped, and he looked sleepy and confused, it was already late at night and he kept running his fingers through his uncombed hair, embarrassed. My great-grandfather and Isaak Baruw walked around the room agitated and arguing; in vain Isaak Baruw spoke calming words, words that reminded my great-grandmother of her lovers. Exhausted, my great-grandmother sank into one of the soft easy chairs and put her cold hands on the samovar. My great-grandfather and Isaak Baruw were speaking Russian, and my great-grandmother didn't understand much more than the words 'second' and 'Petrovsky Park.' The maid was handed a letter and sent out into the dark. At dawn my great-grandfather and Isaak Baruw left the house. My great-grandmother had fallen asleep in the soft easy chair, her small hand and wrist with the red coral bracelet hanging limply. It was as dark and still in the room as on the bottom of the sea.

Toward noon Isaak Baruw came back and, amidst much bowing

and scraping and many condolences, he informed my great-grandmother that my great-grandfather had died at eight o'clock that morning. On the hill in Petrovsky Park, Nikolai Sergeyevich had shot him through the heart.

From *Our Lady of the Assassins*
by Fernando Vallejo

Translated from Spanish by PAUL HAMMOND
Serpent's Tail

Our Lady of the Assassins is an extraordinary autobiographical novel in which a writer, Fernando, returns to the city of Medellín, Colombia, after an absence of many years. There he embarks on a passionate relationship with Alexis, a young male prostitute and hitman.

Did it have any compensation, this torment Alexis put me through, my diurnal exodus through the streets, fleeing the noise and thinking of him? Yes, our nocturnal lovemaking. Our nights bright with passion, me holding my guardian angel tight and him me, as hard as he could, because I must set down here, without braggadocio or presumptuousness, how much he loved me. It's not very charitable, I know, to exhibit your own happiness in front of other people's misfortune, to recount stories of unbridled love to someone who lives as a prisoner, locked up, married, with a prim, fat wife and five kids eating, whining and watching television. But let's leave the TV set on one side and go on, showing our money to the beggar. So what! The poor are poor and Christ died for the truth! Behold us then in the warm silent night, stoking the fire of our love in the summer heat. 'Open the windows, kid,' I asked him, 'and let some air in.' And my baby boy rose naked like a mirage from *The Thousand and One Nights* with his violent imagination and his three scapulars, and opened the French windows. No air entered because there was no air, but there was music, the racket of the freak next door and his pals, the slobs. 'That fucking heavy-metal freak is fucking up our night,' I complained. 'He's not a heavy-metal freak,' Alexis explained to me when I pointed him out in the street the other day, 'he's a punk.' 'Whatever he is, I'd like to kill the bastard.' 'I'll kill him for you,' Alexis told me with that willingness of his, ever attentive to my least whim. 'Leave it to me, next time out comes the piece.' The piece is the revolver. At first I thought it was a knife, but no, it's a revolver. Huh, and I transcribed my baby boy's beloved words badly. He didn't say, 'I'll kill him for you,' he said, 'I'll waste him for you.' They don't conjugate the verb to kill: they go in for its synonyms. The infinite number of synonyms they have for saying it: more than the Arabs have for the camel…

…It was a Tuesday afternoon (because in the morning we'd returned on a pilgrimage to Sabaneta) that the punk 'bought it'. 'There he is! There he is!' exclaimed Alexis when he spotted him in the street. I didn't even have time to stop him. He ran towards the freak, went on ahead of him, half turned, pulled out the revolver and from a few inches away planted a bullet in his forehead, dead centre, right where they mark the holy cross on Ash Wednesday. Blam! A single shot, dry, ineluctable, rotund, that sent the *gonorrea* and his racket to the depths of hell. How many times haven't I played the scene through in my head in slow motion! I see his green eyes watching the punk. Cloudy green. Intoxicated by the uniqueness of the instant. Blam! A single shot, without commentary. Alexis put the revolver away, turned round and carried on walking as if nothing had happened. Why didn't he shoot the guy from behind? In order not to kill treacherously? No, *hombre*, it's to kill looking straight into the victim's eyes…

...I returned to the apartment and after a bit Alexis arrived with a demijohn of *aguardiente*: two and a half bottles of hard liquor in all. 'You might have bought some glasses too,' I pointed out. 'It's obvious there's nothing here to drink out of.' 'From the bottle.' He opened the bottle, took a swig and gave it to me. And so, me drinking from his mouth, he from mine, in the delirium of an absurd life, of an impossible love, of a hatred of others, we put away the demijohn. We woke up in a pool of vomit: it was the demons of Medellín, the accursèd city, which we'd swallowed while walking through its streets and they'd got inside us through the eyes, through the ears, through the nose, through the mouth.

From *Les Liaisons Culinaires*
by Andreas Staïkos

Translated from Greek by ANNE-MARIE STANTON-IFE
The Harvill Press

Dimitris and Damocles, two neighbours in an Athenian block of flats, have discovered that they are both having an affair with the same women, the married Nana. Here, it is Damocles's turn to play suitor…

Potatoes that Melt in the Mouth

And so the two rivals made a pact. They agreed that the one next in line for a date with Nana (Damocles) would call and put her off, pretending that something had come up, and that he would have to leave Athens for a couple of days.

But instead, Damocles decided to dedicate the entire afternoon to the preparation of divine baked potatoes for his beloved Nana. Nothing special. Just one of the most irresistible, albeit familiar dishes in the Greek culinary repertoire: lamb with roast potatoes. After all, it's not *what* you cook, it's *how* you cook it. His potatoes would bowl her over, he would transform the humble, commonplace *pomme de terre* so that she would be unable to recognise the elegant, perfectly formed spheres as potatoes. Perfect spheres the size of tiny marbles just two centimetres in diameter, that would slide between her scarlet lips and dissolve instantly on her tongue, saving her the trouble of having to chew. It would be as though she were drinking them.

Damocles felt good. Taking a small sharp knife, he cut the potatoes into tiny cubes, and then shaped them into balls. But when he had finished the tenth, he began to worry that they all looked the same, and that Nana would suspect that they'd been through a machine. Not easily defeated, he decided to have some fun, cutting the cubes into different sizes and sculpting them into balls between two and three centimetres in diameter. This way he could be sure that they looked handmade, and that a great deal of craftsmanship had gone into them.

He removed the excess fat from the lamb, brushed it with olive oil, seasoned it, and put it in a roasting tin. He arranged the potatoes around the joint and poured two glasses of water, a little olive oil and the juice of two lemons over them. Next he flavoured them with salt, pepper and two finely chopped garlic cloves, and brushed them with olive oil, tossing them well with a wooden spoon. The oven was hot by now. Damocles put the tin in and checked his watch. There was just enough time to make some *baklava*...

...Satisfaction soon turned to ecstasy when Nana, swallowing her first potato declared. 'These are not potatoes. They're kisses. And what kisses! Your kisses – the most divine I've ever tasted! Oh, Damocles, you're going to spoil me! And now I want you to, no, I *demand* that you kiss me, and make sure that your kiss is just a little more delicious than these heavenly potatoes. just a little more irresistible than usual. I know it's not easy, but you will try, won't you? Say you will, Damocles!'

'I'll try, Nana, I'll try,' whispered Damocles in the throes of ecstasy. And he spent almost the whole night, with only a few brief interruptions to moisten his parched, burning lips with a few sips of wine, kissing Nana over and over again, in pursuit of that kiss – the kiss that would be deemed to surpass his potatoes. But he failed.

Nana, however, was very understanding, very supportive.

'Don't despair, Damocles. Don't push yourself so. It doesn't matter, you can try again next time!'

And so it was that poor, hapless Damocles was left with the sweet promise of next time.

****

Oven Roast Lamb and Potatoes

Place a 1½ kg leg (or shoulder) of lamb in the centre of a roasting tin, brushed lightly with olive oil and salt and pepper and wrapped in greaseproof paper or aluminium foil. Take 10 medium-sized potatoes, cut each into 6 to 8 cubes and arrange them around the joint. Add 2 cups of water, [⅓] cup of olive oil, the juice of 2 medium-sized lemons, 3 cloves of garlic and salt and pepper. Stir well. Place the baking tray in a medium-hot oven for 2 hours, turning the potatoes from time to time. Remove the wrapping from the meat to let the potatoes mix with the juices which have collected in the paper. Turn the meat so that it can brown on all sides.

This delicious dish, as tender as Turkish delight, is best set off by a piquant rocket salad.

Rocket Salad

Wash the rocket leaves thoroughly, removing the stalks. Cut the larger leaves in half, pat dry and place in a salad bowl. Add a dressing made up of 3 tablespoons of olive oil, 1½ tablespoons of vinegar, 1 clove of crushed garlic and salt and pepper. Toss well and garnish with deep-red pomegranate seeds.

****

DIFFICULT TIMES

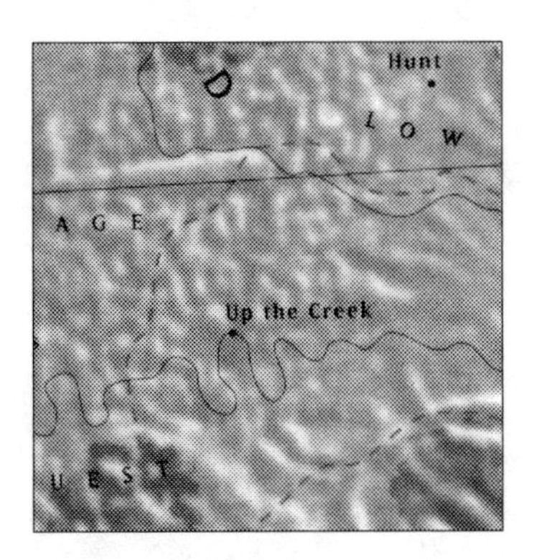

‘At the Beginning’

from *The Triumph of the Water Witch* by Ioana Ieronim

Translated from Romanian by ADAM J. SORKIN with the author
Bloodaxe Books

In *The Triumph of the Water Witch* Romanian poet Ioana Ieronim remembers her childhood in the Transylvanian Saxon part of Rasnov, a small town in the Carpathians, through a series of prose poems. Here she describes her Romanian parents' journey from the ravages of post-war Bucharest to settle in Rasnov.

At the Beginning

The middle of an age adrift, a world at the edge; the crushing war; then convalescence. The world had changed its blood, its garb. You know what they say? They say that after the Transfiguration the waters will turn cooler.

In that poverty drought alarm, my parents, so youthful and fresh, departed from Bucharest, crossed the mountains – and stopped in the broad Bârsa plain, where peace seemed to turn in a more generous circle, vast and sheltering.
For them it was clear, the time to halt had come: their belongings had begun to tumble out of the truck.

Much later, in accordance with their tale, I searched the road for traces of the lion's paws of our chair legs – and it seemed to me I found them.

From *The Carpenter's Pencil*
by Manuel Rivas

Translated from Galician by JONATHAN DUNNE
The Harvill Press

Set in the summer of 1936 during the early months of the Spanish Civil War, *The Carpenter's Pencil* follows the fortunes of imprisoned Galician Republicans, and in particular the heroic, humane doctor Daniel Da Barca. Much of the story is told, years later, by his former guard Herbal, who describes how, even after surviving two firing-squads and a subsequent court-martial and death sentence, Da Barca continues to give solace to his fellow prisoners.

The international campaign for once bore fruit. At the last moment, in response to the government of Cuba's request, Doctor Da Barca had his death sentence commuted to one of life imprisonment.

'In that way he had, he had made himself the prison first-aider, so to speak.' Herbal told Maria da Visitação. 'He was like one of those healers who cure warts from a distance simply by reciting a couple of verses. Even when he had one foot in the grave and was waiting to be executed, he carried on boosting everyone else's spirits.'

The political prisoners functioned as a kind of commune. People who would not talk to each other in the street, who really hated each other, such as Anarchists and Communists, helped each other out inside jail. They even edited an underground newsletter together, which was called *Bungalow*.

The old Republicans, some of them veteran Galicianists from the Celtic Cavern and Brotherhoods of the Language, with the air of old knights of the Round Table, who even received Communion during Mass, acted at times as a council of elders to resolve conflicts and disputes between inmates. There were no more outings without trial. The escorts continued to do their dirty work outside, but the military had decided that a certain discipline should also prevail in the cauldrons of hell. The executions by firing squad did not stop, but the briefest of courts martial would be held first.

With this parallel administration, the prisoners did what they could to improve their situation in jail. They took the initiative on measures of hygiene and the distribution of food. Superimposed on the official timetable was an unwritten calendar, and it was this that effectively governed their daily routines. Tasks were shared out with such organization and efficiency that many ordinary prisoners came to them to ask for help. Behind bars, there was a shadow government, exactly that, a parliament and assembly, and justices of the peace. There was also a school of humanities, a tobacconist's, a joint fund acting as a mutual savings bank, and a hospital.

The prisoners' hospital was Doctor Da Barca.

'There were other staff in the infirmary,' Herbal told Maria da

Visitação, 'but he was the one who carried the burden of responsibility. Even the official doctor, Doctor Soláns, would heed his instructions when visiting, as if he were no more than a chance auxiliary. This Soláns fellow would hardly open his mouth. We all knew he was injecting himself with some drug. You could tell he was sickened by the jail, even though he lived on the outside. He never seemed quite there, stunned by wherever in the world he had come to land in a white coat. Doctor Da Barca, however, knew all the prisoners by name and medical history, whether they were political or not, without the need for keeping records. I don't know how he did it. His head was quicker than an almanac.

'One day an official from the military health inspectorate appeared in the infirmary. He ordered a patient to be examined in his presence. Doctor Soláns was nervous, as if he felt he was being scrutinized. Doctor Da Barca meanwhile stood back, deliberately asking him for advice and handing him the initiative. Suddenly, as he bent to sit down, the official made a strange gesture and a pistol fell out of his shoulder holster. We were there to keep an eye on a prisoner considered dangerous, Genghis Khan. He had been a boxer and a wrestler, and was a bit mad and would suddenly flip. He had been jailed for unintentionally killing a man during a display of freestyle wrestling. He had meant to give him a fright, that was all. From the start of the fight between Genghis Khan and a wrestler called the Lalín Bull, this little man, who was sitting in the front row, had been shouting it was fixed. "It's a fix! It's a fix!" Genghis Khan had blood pouring from his nostrils, he could do that, but still this repulsive little man was not satisfied, as if the spectacle of the wound confirmed his suspicions that the fight was fixed. So then Genghis Khan went berserk. He lifted the Lalín Bull, all twenty stone of him, up in the air and threw him as hard as he could on top of the man shouting that it was a fix, who never felt cheated again.

'So there we all were, in the infirmary, looking at this pistol like it was some dead rat. And Doctor Da Barca said, calm as can be, "My friend, your heart has fallen to the ground." Even that big lad we had the handcuffs on, Genghis Khan, was amazed; then he burst out laughing and said, "You got it, a bloke with three balls!" From that moment on he held Doctor Da Barca in such high esteem that he'd walk beside him in the courtyard each day as if he were covering his back...'

'The War Works Hard'
by Dunya Mikhail

Collected in **A Crack in the Wall: New Arab Poetry**, edited by Margaret Obank & Samuel Shimon, translated from Arabic by the author
Saqi

Dunya Mikhail's poem 'The War Works Hard' represents a rare glimpse of an Iraqi's perspective on recent Gulf conflicts.

The War Works Hard

The war
How serious
    and active
        and skilful
            It is!

From early morning
It wakes up the sirens
    sends ambulances everywhere
    swings corpses in the air
    slides stretchers to the wounded
    summons rain from the eyes of mothers
    digs in the earth
    shovels many things from under the ruins
some lifeless glittering things
others pale and still throbbing

It brings more inquiries
to the minds of children
entertains the gods
by shooting missiles and fireballs
through the sky

It plants mines in the fields
    harvests holes and air-pockets
    urges families to emigrate
    stands with the clergymen
as they curse the devil
        (The wretched one, his hand is still in the fire. It hurts)

The war is relentless, day and night.
It inspires tyrants to give long speeches
    give medals to generals
and themes to poets

It contributes to the industry of artificial limbs
provides food for flies
adds pages to the book of history
achieves equality between victim and murderer
teaches lovers to write letters
trains girls to wait
fills newspapers with stories and photos
beats drums to celebrate every year
builds new houses for orphans
keeps coffin-makers very busy
pats the shoulders of gravediggers
draws a smile on the leader's face.

The war works very hard
without precedent
yet nobody praises it.

From *The 13½ Lives of Captain Bluebear*
by Walter Moers

Translated from German by JOHN BROWNJOHN
Secker & Warburg

Already well-known to German children as an animated television character,Captain Bluebear has been a publishing sensation in its native country. A humorous, witty fantasy, for both adults and children, the book chronicles Bluebear's many adventures in the land of Zamonia, with the help of his trusty encyclopaedia, always straying into danger, always escaping by a paw's breadth. Here, after a long trek across the Demerara Desert, our hero has come across an obstacle: the discarded head of a Bollogg, a monstrous Giant race. In the process of trying to cross the head through one ear and out the other, Bluebear has fallen into a pool of earwax...

...The thing which taxed my ingenuity most of all was the names; there were 150 creature names and around another 150 geographical ones, some of which were gibberish in German, others most straightforward. For instance, the German 'Sugar Desert' became 'Demerara Desert' in English which is more evocative, more alliterative. In many ways translators can now and then improve on the original...

John Brownjohn on translating
The 13½ Lives of Captain Bluebear

The evil-smelling sludge encompassed me like a huge, greasy hand and drew me down. I thrashed around wildly with my forelegs – not a very well-considered course of action, but at least it kept me on the surface. My desperate doggy-paddling even brought me a little closer to the opposite bank of the earwax pool.

Sprouting from the bank and trailing into the pool was a clump of black hairs the thickness of a finger. As I paddled towards it with all my might, the earwax closed over my head and found its way into my nose, eyes and ears, rendering me temporarily blind and deaf. I even swallowed a substantial helping of the sludge – the most disgusting sensation I ever experienced.

In my horror and disgust I forgot to paddle and sank still deeper into the soft, warm ooze. All that now protruded from the pool was one of my paws, which groped for the clump of hairs. My final movement was less of a grab than a farewell wave. I was utterly exhausted.

Someone or something – it was hard to tell which in such a predicament – grasped my paw. At least it didn't feel like a flea's antenna or anything else of an insectlike nature, so I clung to it and allowed myself to be hauled to the surface. I hung on tight and lashed out with my hind legs until they encountered terra firma. Then I crawled out of the pool on all fours and wiped the earwax from my eyes to see who had saved my life. A transparent, pulsating blob of light, it made – even at first sight – a strangely despondent impression.

'My name is 1600H,' it said. 'I'm an idea.'

'Delighted to meet you,' I replied. 'My name is Bluebear, and I'm a bluebear.'

We stood there rather awkwardly for a while, at a loss to know what to say next. For want of a better idea, I started to wring the earwax out of my fur.

'You were lucky I happened to be nearby,' the idea said. 'Many people have drowned in that pool. Bollogg earwax is treacherous stuff.'

'You can say that again. Many thanks, you saved my life. I owe you one.'

'Don't mention it. I'm glad to have been of service for once. I'm not much use as a rule.'

'How do you mean?'

'Well, I'm an idea, but a bad one. Everyone began by making a tremendous fuss of me, but they eventually discovered that I wasn't a good idea. When that happens, people simply drop you. There are masses of us roaming the passages in this brain. We're the dregs of the cerebral community. Could *you* find a use for a bad idea?'

'I'm not sure. All I'd like to know is the quickest way through the head and out the other side.'

'You don't need an idea for that, you've already got one: "*Through the head and out the other side.*" Whether or not it's a good idea I couldn't say. It's diabolically difficult and dangerous, getting from one side of the brain to the other. Do you know how many miles of cerebral convolutions there are in here?'

'No.'

'Neither do I, but there must be millions of them.'

That was an exaggeration, I suspected, but I was beginning to realize that the whole business wasn't as simple as I'd thought.

'What you need is a plan – a plan of this brain, so you don't lose your way. A plan made by a planmaker, I mean. Do you follow me?'

'No.'

'The plans in this brain are made by planmakers. They're good craftsman but very fussy. If you need a shoe you go to a shoemaker. If you need a plan you go to a planmaker. I know one who lives quite near here. Like me to take you to him?'

Ideas, so 1600H told me, took their names from the hour, minute and second at which they occurred to someone. Most such names were much longer, for instance 2346H/46M/12S or 1321H/32M/55S, and so on, but 1600H really had originated on the stroke of 4pm

'The trouble is, lots of us have the same name. After all, new ideas crop up almost every second of every day. I know fifty other ideas named 1600H, and guess what? They're all equally bad. Four pm doesn't seem a particularly favourable time for good ideas...'

...We were now in yet another passage, a big tunnel along whose walls minute specks of light were racing like demented sparklers. The sparks seemed to have voices, faint but clearly audible little voices that whispered or muttered, murmured or giggled as they sped past us. They varied in size and colour, some being white and others red or green. They came from all directions, from behind and ahead, above and below, making me feel as if I were in the middle of a miniature firework display. Sometimes two sparks collided, combined to produce a dazzling flash, and raced on into the darkness, chattering together. I paused to stare in amazement, turning my head this way and that like a spectator at a tennis match.

1600H answered my unspoken question. 'They're thoughts,' he said. 'We're now inside the Bollogg's brain.'

From the '*Encyclopaedia of Marvels, Life Forms and Other Phenomena of Zamonia and its Environs*'
by Professor Abdullah Nightingale

Bollogg Thoughts. Strictly speaking, these are any ideas promoted by means of cerebral activity from a Bollogg's realm of perception and sensation to that of the conceptual, judgemental, and inferential. In a wider sense, however, they are ideas relating to matters not directly perceived by a Bollogg or possibly inaccessible to its senses; in other words, ideas conjured up not only by the power of memory but also by the Bollogg's imaginative faculty...

...1600H pointed to the specks of light flitting along the wall of the tunnel.

'There are a lot of different ideas in here, you can tell them apart by their colours. The red ones are commonplace, everyday ideas – those are in the majority. The yellow ones are worries, of which there are also plenty. The blue are questions the brain keeps asking, and the green are answers. If a blue question collides with a wrong green answer, absolutely nothing happens.'

Just then a green flash collided with a blue one, setting off a few sparks. They circled each other in a puzzled kind of way before whizzing off again.

'You see? If the blue question bumped into the correct green answer, they'd merge and become a solution. See that big orange flash there? That's a solution.'

In fact, several of these orange flashes were racing along the wall of the tunnel. 1600H drove his fist into his palm.

'If two solutions collide they produce an idea – a good one or a bad one, whichever. I'm a bad one.' He sighed. 'Here comes a good one.' A glowing blob of light rounded the bend a few feet behind us. At least twice the size of 1600H, it was lit up from within like a Christmas tree and hummed like an electricity pylon as it strode majestically past us.

'Hello, 1600H,' it said in a condescending tone.

'Hello, 2100H/36M/14S,' 1600H replied humbly.

'How does a Bollogg manage to have a good idea?' I asked. 'I thought Bolloggs were mentally rather ill-equipped.'

We were walking side by side along the tunnel, which seemed to meander on for ever. At brief intervals, numerous neuron paths branched off it to left and right. Meanwhile, we were surrounded by a continuous, multicoloured stream of racing thoughts, questions, answers, and solutions.

'They don't become stupid until they remove their heads. The heads themselves are far from daft. Only the bodies are stupid.'

'Then why did this one remove his head, if he was so intelligent?' 1600H glowed red for a moment. He hummed and hawed, then:

'Well... That was one of his bad ideas...'

'Why are you blushing?' I asked.

1600H groaned. 'To be quite honest, the bad idea was me.'

From *Soul Mountain*
by Gao Xingjian

Translated from Chinese by MABEL LEE
Flamingo

Gao Xingjian's poetic, autobiographical novel *Soul Mountain* won him the 2000 Nobel Prize for Literature. In 1982, following a false diagnosis of lung cancer, as well as the ever-present threat of political repression, Gao left Beijing and travelled for five months through China, an epic journey of some 15,000 kilometres. This journey later resulted in the publication of his 'novel' *Soul Mountain*, an account of just such a journey. Here Gao recalls the terror of his cancer diagnosis – and the moment he realized he'd been reprieved.

I didn't know whether, during my lifetime, others had wronged me more or I had wronged others more. I knew however that there were people such as my deceased mother who really loved me, and people such as my estranged wife who really hated me, but was there any need to settle accounts in the few days left to me? For those I had wronged my death could count as a sort of compensation and for those who had wronged me I was powerless to do anything. Life is probably a tangle of love and hate permanently knotted together. Could it have any other significance? But to hastily end it just like this was too soon. I realized that I had not lived properly. If I did have another lifetime, I would definitely live it differently, but this would require a miracle.

I didn't believe in miracles, just like I didn't believe in fate, but when one is desperate, isn't a miracle all that could be hoped for?

Fifteen days later I arrived at the hospital for my X-ray appointment. My younger brother was anxious and insisted, against my wishes, on coming with me. I didn't like showing my emotions to people close to me. If I were on my own it would be easier to control myself, but I couldn't change his mind and he came anyway. A classmate from middle school was at the hospital and he took me straight to the head doctor of the X-ray section.

The head doctor as usual was wearing his glasses and sitting in his swivel chair. He read the diagnosis on my medical record, examined the two chest X-rays and said that an X-ray from the side would have to be taken. He immediately wrote a note for another X-ray, and said the wet X-ray should be brought to him as soon as the image had developed.

The autumn sun was splendid. It was cold inside and sitting there looking through the window at the sun shining on the grass, I thought it was even more wonderful. I had never looked at the sunshine this way before. After the side position X-ray, I sat looking at the sunshine outside while waiting by the darkroom for the film to develop. The sunshine outside the window was actually too distant from me, I should have been thinking about what was immediately to take place right here. But did I need to think a lot about that? My situation was like that of a murderer with cast-iron evidence against him waiting for the judge to pass the death sentence. All I could hope for was a miracle. Didn't the two damn chest X-rays taken by two separate hospitals at two different times provide the evidence for condemning me to death?

I didn't know when it was, I wasn't even aware of it, probably it was while I was staring out of the window at the sunshine, that I heard myself silently intoning, take refuge in Namo Amitofu, Buddha. I had been doing this for quite some time. It seemed I had already been praying from the time I put on my clothes and left the execution chamber, the X-ray room with the equipment for raising and lowering patients as they lay there.

In the past, I would certainly have considered it preposterous to think that one day I would be praying. I used to be filled with pity when I saw old people in temples burning incense, kneeling in prayer, and quietly intoning Namo Amitofu. My pity was quite different from sympathy. If I were to verbalize this reaction, it would probably be: Ah! Pitiful wretches, they're old and if their insignificant wishes aren't realized, they pray that they will be realized in their hearts. However I thought it was ridiculous for a robust young man or a pretty young woman to be praying and whenever I heard young devotees intoning Namo Amitofu I would want to laugh, and clearly not without malice. I couldn't understand how people in the prime of life could do such a stupid thing but now I have prayed, prayed devoutly, and from the depths of my heart. Fate is unyielding and humans are so frail and weak. In the face of misfortune man is nothing.

While awaiting the pronouncement of the death sentence, I was in this state of nothingness, looking at the autumn sun outside the window, silently intoning Namo Arnitofu, over and over, in my heart.

My old schoolmate, who couldn't wait any longer, knocked and went into the darkroom. My brother followed him in but was sent out and had to stand by the window where the X-rays came out, Soon my schoolmate also came out and went to the window to wait. They had transferred their concern for the prisoner to the documentation of his sentence, an inappropriate metaphor. Like an onlooker who had nothing to do with it, I watched as they went into the darkroom, keeping in my heart Namo Amitofu which I silently intoned over and over again. Then, suddenly I heard them shouting out in surprise:

'What?'

'Nothing?'

'Check again!'

'There's only been this one side chest X-ray all afternoon.' The response from the darkroom was unfriendly.

The two of them pegged the X-ray onto a frame and held it up for inspection. The darkroom technician also came out, looked at it, made an offhand remark, then dismissed them.

Buddha said rejoice. Buddha said rejoice first replaced Namo Amitofu, then turned into more common expressions of sheer joy and elation. This was my initial psychological reaction after I had extricated myself from despair, I was really lucky. I had been blessed by Buddha and a miracle had taken place. But my joy was furtive, I did not dare to appear hasty.

I was still anxious and took the wet X-ray for verification by the head doctor with the glasses.

He looked at the X-ray and threw up both of his arms in grand theatrical style.

'Isn't this wonderful?'

'Do I still have to have that done?' I was asking about the final X- ray.

'Still have to have what done?' he berated me, he saved people's lives and had this sort of authority.

He then got me to stand in front of an X-ray machine with a projector screen and told me to take a deep breath, breathe out, turn around, turn to the left, turn to the right.

'You can see it for yourself,' he said, pointing to the screen. 'Have a look, have a look.'

Actually I didn't seen anything clearly, my brain was like a great blob of paste and the only thing I saw on the screen was a blurry rib cage.

'There's nothing there, is there?' he loudly berated me as if I were deliberately being a nuisance.

'But then how can those other X-rays be explained?' I couldn't stop myself asking.

'If there's nothing there, there's nothing there, it's just vanished. How can it be explained? Colds and lung inflammation can cause a shadow and when you get better, the shadow disappears.'

But I hadn't asked him about a person's state of mind. Could that cause a shadow?

'Go and live properly, young man.' He swivelled his chair around, dismissing me.

He was right, I had won a new lease of life, I was younger than a new-born baby...

...For me, however, what I had to ponder was this: How should I change this life for which I had just won a reprieve?

CALM OLD AGE

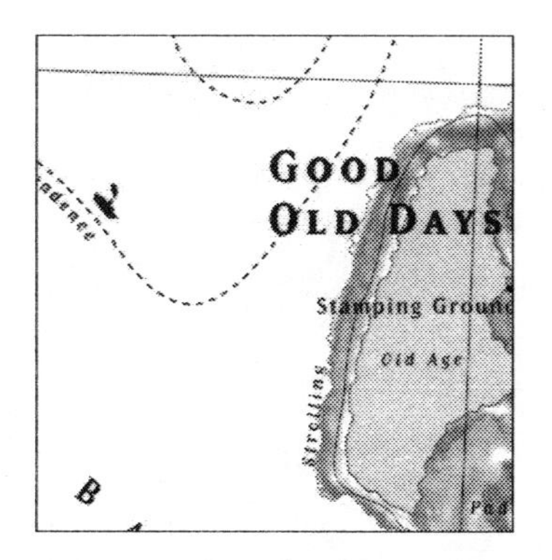

'The Eyes'

from *The Eyes: A version of Antonio Machado* by Don Paterson

Faber & Faber

Don Paterson's collection *The Eyes* presents a spiritual portrait of the great Spanish poet Antonio Machado (1873–1939), which lies somewhere between translation and imitation. The following, the title poem of the collection, is Paterson's version of Machado's most famous work.

Literal translation can be useful in providing us with a black-and-white snapshot of the original but a version – however subjectively – seeks to restore a light and colour perspective…

Don Paterson on translating Machado's poetry

The Eyes

When his beloved died
he decided to grow old
and shut himself inside
in the empty house, alone
with his memories of her
and the big sunny mirror
where she'd fixed her hair.
This great block of gold
he hoarded like a miser,
thinking here, at least,
he'd lock away the past,
keep one thing intact.

But around the first anniversary,
he began to wonder, to his horror,
about her eyes: *Were they brown or black,*
or grey? Green? Christ! I can't say...

One Spring morning, something gave in him;
shouldering his twin grief like a cross,
he shut the front door, turned into the street
and walked just ten yards, when, from a dark close,
he caught a flash of eyes. He lowered his hat-brim
and walked on...*yes, they were like that; like that...*

From *Portrait in Sepia*
by Isabel Allende

Translated from Spanish by MARGARET SAYERS PEDEN
Flamingo

Portrait in Sepia, set at the end of the nineteenth century in Chile, is peopled by characters from Isabel Allende's previous celebrated novels, *Daughter of Fortune* and *The House of the Spirits*. Narrated by Aurora del Valle, a spirited young woman in search of her family roots – and the key to a childhood trauma, it tells the story of the del Valle family, and in particular her ambitious and regal grandmother, Paulina del Valle, who not only marries her former butler, Frederick Williams, after the death of her husband but starts her own vineyard in old age. When she succumbs to cancer she travels, undaunted, with Aurora to the Hobbs Clinic in London to find a cure.

During that crossing of the cordillera of the Andes, and later on the ocean liner, I was able to observe my grandmother closely, and I became aware that something basic was beginning to weaken in her, something that wasn't her will, her mind, or her greed, something more like her ferocity. She became gentle, bland, and so absentminded that she used to stroll on the deck of the ship dressed in fine muslin and pearls, but without her false teeth. It was obvious that she had bad nights: she had deep circles beneath her eyes and was always sleepy. She had lost a lot of weight, and her skin hung loose when she removed her corset. She wanted me to stay very close, 'So you don't flirt with the sailors,' she said, a cruel joke since at that age my shyness was so absolute that one innocent look in my direction from a man and I would blush like a boiled lobster. The real reason was that Paulina del Valle felt fragile, and she needed me at her side to distract her from death. She didn't mention her health: to the contrary, she talked about spending a few days in London and then going on to France to see about the barrels and cheese, but I guessed from the beginning that she had other plans. That became apparent as soon as we arrived in England and she began her diplomatic labour of convincing Frederick Williams to go on alone; we would stay to shop a while and then join him later. I don't know whether Williams went ahead without suspecting that his wife was ill, or whether he guessed the truth, and understanding her modesty, left her in peace. The fact is that he checked us into the Hotel Savoy, and once he was sure we didn't lack for anything, he took the next ferry across the channel, but without any enthusiasm.

My grandmother did not want witnesses to her decline, and she was especially reserved in front of Williams. That was part of the coquettishness she acquired once they were married; she'd shown none of that when he was her butler. She'd had no reluctance then to expose to him the worst side of her character, and he saw her dressed any which way, but from the day of their marriage she'd tried to impress him with her best plumage. That autumnal relationship was very important to her, and she didn't want bad health to damage the solid edifice of her vanity, which was why she tried to keep her husband at a distance, and if I hadn't planted my feet, she would have shut me out too. It was a battle to be allowed to go with her on those medical visits but finally she yielded, given my stubbornness and her weakness. She was in pain, and almost couldn't swallow, but she didn't seem frightened, although she sometimes made jokes about the drawbacks of hell and boredom of heaven. The Hobbs clinic inspired confidence from the moment you stepped inside, with its hall filled with bookshelves and oil portraits of the surgeons who had practiced within those walls. We were received by an impeccable matron and led to the doctor's office, a cozy room with elegant brown leather furniture and a fireplace where large logs were crackling. Dr Gerald Suffolk's appearance was as impressive as his fame. He was a Teutonic type, large and ruddy, with a thick scar on his cheek that instead of making him ugly made him unforgettable. On his desk were the letters he had exchanged with my grandmother, the records of the Chilean specialists she had consulted, and the package with the rubber gloves, which she had sent ahead that morning by messenger. Later we learned that was an unnecessary precaution, since they had been used in the Hobbs clinic for three years. Suffolk welcomed us as if we were on a social call, offering us Turkish coffee scented with cardamom seeds. He led my grandmother to an adjoining room and after examining her returned to the office and leafed through a weighty book while she dressed. The patient soon returned, and the surgeon confirmed the earlier diagnosis of her Chilean doctors: my grandmother had a gastrointestinal tumor. He added that the operation would be risky for someone of her age, and also because it was in the experimental stage, but he had developed a perfect technique for such cases, and physicians came from all over the world to learn from him...My grandmother surprised Dr Suffolk when she demanded that he explain in detail what he intended to do to her; he was accustomed to having patients deliver themselves unto the unquestioned authority of his hands with the passivity of hens, but he seized the occasion to display his erudition with a lecture, more concerned with impressing us with the virtuosity of his scalpel than with the well-being of his unfortunate patient. He drew a sketch of intestines and organs that resembled a demented machine, and pointed out to us where the tumor was located and how he planned to excise it, right down to the type of suture, information that Paulina del Valle listened to imperturbably but so undid me I had to leave the office. I sat in the hall of the portraits to pray quietly. In truth I was more afraid for myself than for her…

…Contrary to all my pessimistic predictions, my grandmother survived the surgery, and after the first week, during which her fever rose and dropped uncontrollably, she stabilized and could begin to eat solid foods. I never left her side except to go to the hotel once a day to bathe and change my clothes, because the smell of the anaesthetics, medications, and disinfectants produced a viscous mixture that clung to the skin. I slept in fits and starts, sitting in a chair beside the patient. Ignoring my grandmother's strict injunction, I sent a telegram to Frederick Williams the day of the operation, and he arrived in London thirty hours later. I saw him lose his proverbial composure beside the bed where his wife lay stupefied by drugs, moaning with each breath, toothless, nearly hairless: a parchment-skinned old woman He knelt beside her and placed his forehead upon the bloodless hand of Paulina del Valle, whispering her name, and when he got up his face was wet with tears. My grandmother, who maintained that youth is not a period in life but a state of mind, and that you have the health you deserve, looked totally defeated in that hospital bed. That woman, whose appetite for life was as colossal as her gluttony, had turned her face to the wall, indifferent to everything around her, immersed in herself. Her enormous strength of will, her vigour, her curiosity, her sense of adventure, even her greed, had been erased by her physical suffering...

Paulina del Valle must have had the strength of an ox; they opened her stomach, removed a tumor the size of a grapefruit, sewed her up like a shoe, and within a couple of months she was her old self. All that remained of that amazing adventure was a pirate's scar across her belly and a voracious appetite for life and, of course, food. We left for France as soon as she able to walk without a cane. She completely discarded the diet recommended by Dr Suffolk; as she said, she hadn't come to Paris from an ass-backward corner of the world to eat baby pap. Using the pretext of studying the manufacture of cheese, she stuffed herself with every delicacy that country could offer.

From *Dirty Havana Trilogy*
by Pedro Juan Gutiérrez

Translated from Spanish by NATASHA WIMMER
Faber & Faber

In Pedro Juan Gutiérrez's autobiographical novel *Dirty Havana Trilogy* Pedro Juan, a down-on-his-luck ex-radio journalist, wanders through the city's streets from one dead-end job, one dead-end sexual encounter, to the next. Along the way he describes life on the underbelly of Havana, portraying vice, poverty and desperation in modern Cuba – and the characters he meets along the way.

He was a tough old guy. A very old black man. Ravaged but not completely destroyed. He lived at 558 San Lázaro, and he spent every day sitting silently in his wheelchair in the doorway, watching the traffic, breathing in gasoline fumes, and selling boxes of cigarettes slightly cheaper than in the stores. I bought a pack from him, opened it, and offered it to him, but he refused. I offered him rum, but he wouldn't take that either. I was in a good mood. Now that I had a little money in my pocket, a bottle of rum, and a pack of cigarettes, I was beginning to see the world in a new light. I told the old man that, and we talked for a while. I had half a bottle of rum in me, and that made me chatty and entertaining. An hour and a few drinks later (finally he agreed to have a drink with me), the old man gave me an in: he used to work in the theater.

'Where? At the Martí?'

'No. At the Shanghai.'

'Ah. And what did you do there? I've heard it was a strip joint. Is it true that they shut it down as soon as the Revolution began?'

'Yes, but I hadn't been working there long. I was Superman. There was always a poster just for me: "The one and only Superman, exclusive engagement at this theater." Do you know how long my prick was when it was fully erect? Twelve inches. I was a freak. That's how they advertised me: "A freak of nature...Superman...twelve inches – thirty centimetres – one foot of Superprick...appearing now...Superman!..."'

...'And why did you give it up?'

'Because that's life. Sometimes you're up and sometimes you're down. By the time I was thirty-two or so, the jets of come weren't as strong and then there were times when I lost concentration and sometimes my prick would droop a little and straighten up again. Lots of nights, I couldn't come at all. By then I was half-crazy, because I had spent so many years straining my brain. I took Spanish fly, ginseng; in the Chinese pharmacy on Zanja, they made me a tonic that helped, but it made me jittery. No one could understand the toll my career was taking on me. I had a wife. We were together for our whole lives, more or less, from the time I came to Havana until she died a few months ago. Well, during all of that time, I was never able to come with her. We never had children. My wife didn't see my jism in twelve years. She was a saint. She knew that if we fucked as God willed and I came, then at night I wouldn't be able to do my number at the Shanghai. I had to save up my jism for twenty-four hours to do the Superman show.'

'Incredible self-control.'

'It was either control myself or die of hunger. It wasn't easy to make money in those days.'

'It's still hard.'

'Yes. The poor are born to be shit on.'

'And what happened then?'

'Nothing. I stayed at the theater for a while longer, doing filler; I put together a little skit with the blond girl, and people liked it. They advertised us as "Superprick and the Golden Blonde, the horniest couple in the world." But it wasn't the same. I earned very little. Then I joined a circus. I was a clown, I took care of the lions I was a base-man for the balancing acts. A little bit of everything. My wife was a seamstress, and she cooked. For years, that's what we did. In the end, life is crazy. It takes many unexpected turns.'

We had another drink from the bottle. He let me stay there that night, and the next day I got him some porn magazines...He leafed through them.

'These have been outlawed for thirty-five years. In this country a person is practically forbidden to laugh. I used to like these.'

...'And don't you like these magazines anymore, Superman? Keep them, they're a gift.'

'No, son, no. What good will they do me now? ... Look.'

He lifted up the small blanket that covered his stumps. He no longer had prick or balls. Everything had been amputated along with his lower limbs. It was all chopped off, all the way up to his hip bones. There was nothing left. A little rubber hose came out of the spot where his prick used to be and let fall a steady drip of urine into a plastic bag he carried tied at his waist.

'What happened to you?'

'High blood sugar. The gangrene crept up my legs. And little by little, they were amputated. They even took my balls. Now I really don't have any balls! Ha ha ha. I used to be ballsy. The Superman of the Shanghai! Now I'm fucked, but no one can take away what I've had.'

And he laughed heartily. Not even a hint of irony. I got along well with that tough old man, who knew how to laugh at himself. That's what I'd like: to learn to laugh at myself. Always, even if they cut off my balls.

‘Cat Out of Hell’
from *Cusan Dyn Dall/Blind Man’s Kiss* by Menna Elfyn

Translated from Welsh by GILLIAN CLARKE
Bloodaxe Books

Menna Elfyn’s *Cusan Dyn Dall/Blind Man’s Kiss*, a bilingual Welsh/English poetry collection, explores Welsh identity with passion, realism – and humour.

Cat Out of Hell
(93 year old Ada Berk was caught speeding…)

She was born to a quill by candlelight
in the century of discretion,
the old world where walking
behind a scythe was intuition

Then came the singing machine.
Some took to it like birds to the sky.
Said Ada when they flagged her down,
'What use are wings but to fly?'

'Ada Berk, you'll hit big trouble,'
said the speed cop through the window,
'calling everybody honey,
and you a widow.'

'Well, honey boy, I've nobody left
to call me darling any more.
And where's the sense on a winding lane
dawdling at 60. It's hedgehog law.

Only once a month I can pay for my wheels,
never mind getting speedy.'
Now she's stuck in a rut steering
meals-on-wheels to the old and needy.

Sentenced for speeding, fast Ada
does community service, no wage,
on wheels that loiter wherever they go
to pay for not acting her age.

...AND IN THE END

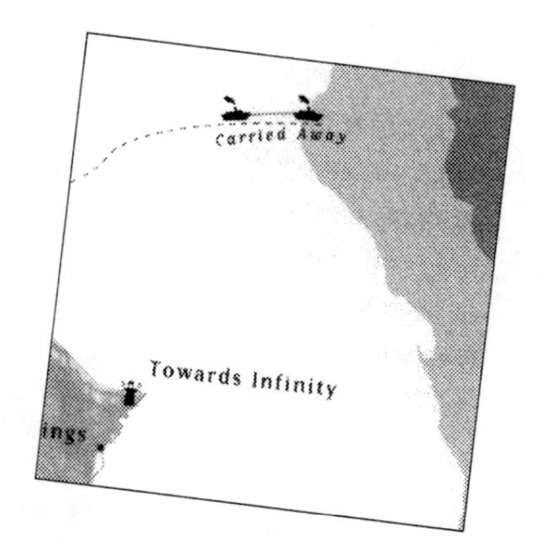

'Postcard (4)'
from *Camp Notebook* by Miklós Radnóti

Translated from Hungarian by FRANCIS R. JONES
Arc

An extraordinary and unique collection of poems, Hungarian poet Miklós Radnóti's *Camp Notebook* was written in secret – often on scraps of paper or labels – during his incarceration in Nazi slave-labour camps during the war. After his death, shot on a forced march in 1944 in the western Hungarian town of Abda, his body was exhumed and the poems found in his pocket. 'Postcard (4)', written on an olive-oil bottle label, is the last poem in the collection, and describes the shooting of Radnóti's friend, the violinist Miklós Lorthy, a few days before Radnóti's own, all too similar death.

Postcard (4)

I tumbled beside him, his body twisted and then,
like a snapped string, up it sprang again.
Neck shot. 'This is how you'll be going too,'
I whispered to myself, 'just lie easy now.'
Patience is blossoming into death.
'Der springt noch auf,' rang out above me. Mud
dried on my ear, mingled with blood.

Szentkirályszabadja, 31st Oct 1944

From *As the Crow Flies*
by Véronique Tadjo

Translated from French by WANGŨI WA GORO
Heinemann

Following a passionate love affair that has turned sour, the narrator of *As the Crow Flies* offers a variety of stories in many different voices – news reports, allegories, ancestral legends, as well as tales of everyday existence – whose record of suffering, parting, desire and healing gradually achieve a mythic status. Here a couple face illness and death together.

She has been writhing and battling with the pain for three days. The sheets, which had been changed, were already drenched in sweat. A soft light bathed the small room. The flowers had opened and some petals littered the small bed-side table.

He looked at her and he knew that he loved her more than ever. He could hear her weak and regular breathing which echoed like a distant refrain. How long he remained like that looking at her suffering, he did not know. How long he was going to remain there like that, helpless, feeling her trickle away, he did not know.

He felt like screaming, so loud that the sound would pierce the walls, its reverberations would silence the city and time would recoil. He wanted to submit his body to the same suffering – feel this pain which now replaced pleasure.

Then, he prayed. He knelt down and prayed. He had not done this in a long time. There was an age when simple words lifted fear. Days when time was not of the essence. Now he was hesitant. He had a strong longing for his childhood prayers.

He placed his hands together, not so much to call to a god, but more to gather his strength. He stayed like this until evening. When the last sounds had been heard and the city seemed to be sleeping, he looked at her and found that she had woken up.

'I will go with you to death,' he said to her. 'I want to love you till the end of your suffering.'

'You cannot stop death,' she murmured. 'It is too strong. Do you remember Orpheus and Eurydice? What shall we do in this city, abandoned to despair and non-believers? You know it: the disease is devouring me.'

'I'll go to the end of our story.'

'Very well,' she said, and she fell asleep again.

Then he picked her up in his arms and walked through the city. He crossed deserted neighbourhoods. He walked above roads, above rooftops, through the green foliage of the trees. After travelling for several days and nights, he was exhausted. He placed her on some thick grass in a garden.

'Don't be afraid, I won't leave you. There is still a long way to go, but together, it should be easier. Drink some water, it will make you feel better.'

He gave her water, which she drank in small sips, and when she had finished, they continued on their way. She dozed in his arms. This time he crossed streams, small and large rivers, he hopped across swamps and ran on lakes.

They came to the sea. They marvelled at what they saw, and she said:

'I want to die here. What can be more beautiful than this dancing foam and engulfing water?'

'No, please, not yet,' he said and he listened to the waves which seemed to show him the way.

They travelled for seven more days as far as the white mountains. The silence and cold were one. The awesome void swallowed all vision.

'I could not die anywhere else. This is where peace lies. Just look at immensity where no impurity can stain death. Even the soil rests beneath the cold. My body will retain its youth. The passing centuries count for nothing. Leave me here.'

'No,' he said, looking at her with compassion. 'This solitude chills my soul. I could never leave your body on this carpet of ice. I would feel as though I had betrayed you.'

He still had a long way to go on this painful journey. But then, before he came to the desert, they knew they had now reached the end of the earth and there was nowhere else for them to go. She looked him straight in the eyes:

'This is it. Now leave me. I must cross the desert gates alone. Beyond those are the souls of the dead. There is nothing more that you can do. Following me would be futile.'

His heart began to race. He suddenly felt that he was going to lose her.

'Let me love you one last time.'

And so it was there, between the earth and the sky, that they loved each other so intensely that the sun was eclipsed and a cool wind swept their bodies.

In the morning, she lay dead.

From *Dunyazad*
by May Telmissany,

translated from Arabic by Roger Allen
Saqi

May Telmissany's semi-autobiographical novella, *Dunyazad*, is the story of a woman who loses her child at birth. Set against the backdrop of Egypt's new middle-class and its crushing will to conform, the book explores her loss, as well as her slow and agonized process of recovery, both physical and psychological. In this extract, both parents try to come to terms with the initial shock of Dunyazad's death, although the narrator's husband knows something she, as yet, does not; that their child died in her womb before she'd given birth.

...The translators of Dunyazad worked with the author herself on the translations...After two days of reading we came to the end of her work, and at the final page the author declared herself unable to read the final section out loud. And, with that emotional moment, the linkage of the narrative whose features we had been discussing in such detached terms to the living person of its author struck home with a tremendous impact...

Roger Allen on translating *Dunyazad*

A sunny Wednesday morning. We opened the window and the sound of birds came bursting in. We packed our suitcases to leave. I asked my husband to check on Dunyazad. He cautioned me that by now she might be dead. We agreed that in spite of everything I should still see her. I said I would rather she died than live in unbearable pain. I was only trying to reassure him; I just wanted that tiny head of hers to be given a supply of oxygen and returned to its natural state. I waited for him to bring her to me in her embroidered white dress. I smiled and found self-assurance in my inner feelings and the gentle breeze wafting in through the window. 'A lovely, sunny day; no one can die today.'

The doctor's report noted that death had occurred inside the womb due to a total rupture of the placenta. I put the report into my pocket and went to the local health office. I got a burial licence, then hurried back. As usual she was waiting for me. The curtains were closed, and the room was shrouded in her silence. Everyone was waiting outside room 401, occasionally exchanging snippets of conversation. No name for the baby was recorded on the documents, so I couldn't say her name, something I'd wanted to do for years.

'Zad-al-Rimal' (food of the sands), she whom my eyes had yet to see.

I remember my wife going to see the sonar specialist twice. I didn't go with her; now I can't recall why. Shebab al-Din went with her and saw a set of jumbled images that he proceeded to arrange in his young mind. He loved her, it seems, without even knowing it or realizing that now he was an only child again.

My husband left the room. I looked towards the window, waiting and listening apprehensively. He came back alone and sat on the edge of the bed. It's all over, he said, and hugged me. I stifled my screams. So the day had lied to me; so had the sun and birds. This wasn't a lovely day. Everyone said: you would have died for sure; it was a sudden haemorrhage; another half-hour in the operating theatre, and there would have been the risk of gangrene; blood-pouches dangling by my bed, glucose, and an intravenous needle. I can't believe it. The pain recedes, the danger symptoms diminish, and still there's the wait for the baby girl. In spite of everything she arrived, and my womb was never her grave.

After a while three nurses came in with a tiny white bundle; everything was absolutely discreet. We shouldn't defile a body once it's been wrapped in a shroud. 'Don't scream,' my husband warned me. I wanted to hold her in my arms, but they refused and took her away without my even realizing it. One of the nurses stayed with me, but I asked her to leave me alone. I told her I was fine.

She was fine when I left her. There was no screaming in the room. I didn't let her hold the tiny shroud. I wanted to do it myself, but I didn't. We hurried. My mind was drilled for what had to be done. We drove calmly to the graveyard in my elder brother's car; I sat beside him, and the basket of roses was on the back seat beside my mother. A tiny procession with no one but us. I wondered what the youngsters would do when we got to the graveyard, and panicked as I contemplated what might happen to interfere with our task.

An eerie quiet. The graveyard was empty, and the winding road seemed burdened by the end of a hot spring. The shroud was lowered on its own, and the basket of roses was left for the small children.

My husband's mother arrived, then my own mother. We got everything ready to leave the hospital. Two days out of life; the spectre of inexorable death infiltrates the very pores of the room.

At the main door of the hospital I spotted the security man in his blue uniform. Two days ago he'd smiled at me as I'd been walking round and round the hospital vestibule trying to rid myself of the constant pain.

I huddle up on my own in the waiting car. Four years ago, I remember, I was holding my first child. The sun was shining in through the window. As he lay there in my arms, I was overcome by a childish sense of exultation. But this time those arms are empty. My womb feels its loss, and I am left to agonize over the gaping wound and emptiness inside me. As we head for home, everything is silence.

I drink a bottle of juice, lean back on a small pillow, and try to get some sleep in the car. We take our son home too; he had come with his grandmother and was settled in the front seat. 'Shehab's baby sister has gone back in Mummy's tummy,' he said with all the conviction of his four years, 'so she can get bigger.' Then he added: 'Get well, Mummy dear!'

As we drove home I told myself I'd give her all the details when the time was right. I bought plenty of cartons of juice and a few other things. I began to wonder when our daughter had actually been born and when she'd died. According to my wife, Dunyazad was born at approximately three thirty in the afternoon on 15 May 1995 and died on 16 May in the evening. She also said, 'my womb wasn't her grave for a single day,' but I knew otherwise. On the way home I turned towards her and gave her a pat on the legs. That dreadful question kept pounding away: when was our daughter really born, the one I'd watched a few hours earlier being lowered into an underground vault?

From *Death and the Penguin*
by Andrey Kurkov

Translated from Russian by GEORGE BIRD
The Harvill Press

Andrey Kurkov's *Death and the Penguin* is set in the Ukraine – a new country with a crumbling infrastructure, at the mercy of Mafia gangsters. Viktor, a would-be writer, lives alone in Kiev with his pet penguin Misha, rescued after the closure of the city zoo. When the editor-in-chief of a major newspaper commissions him to write obituaries of local VIPs to be kept on file in the event of their deaths, he accepts eagerly. But when his subjects begin to die in suspicious circumstances, his enthusiasm wanes and soon he and his penguin are drawn into a bizarre web of Mob dealings. Here, Viktor – and Misha – attend the funeral of Pidpaly, a friendly local penguinologist, although it seems that even at the cemetery they can't escape suspicious characters.

The funeral bus jolted mercilessly. The driver tried to drive slowly, but flashy foreign-made cars, in a hurry as always, kept sounding their horns, causing him to keep an anxious eye on his rear-view mirror.

In front sat two intelligent-looking little men, one wearing a short sheepskin coat, the other a black leather jacket, both fiftyish. One was the cosmetician, the other the undertaker, but which was which Viktor didn't know, since they had appeared simultaneously, helping the mortuary orderlies carry out the coffin and shove it through the rear door of the bus.

Viktor sat at the back with an arm around Misha to keep him in his seat. Beside them, creaking as they rounded corners, was the coffin, nailed shut and covered with red and black material.

From time to time he met the inquisitive gaze of the little men, though it was Misha, not him, who was the object of their curiosity.

Arriving at the Baykov Cemetery, they stopped outside the office. The driver went to ask the plot number, and Viktor used this time to buy a large bunch of flowers from one of the old women standing there.

The way through the cemetery avenues seemed surprisingly long, and Viktor found the endless succession of monuments and railings wearying.

The bus stopped.

Viktor got up, preparing to make for the door.

'Not yet,' said the driver, poking his head round the transparent partition.

'Look at that lot! Watch you don't scrape them!' said one of the little men, gazing ahead.

Viktor looked too. The right-hand side of the avenue was lined with flashy foreign-made cars, leaving a tight squeeze for the bus.

'Best make a detour,' said the driver. 'Out of harm's way.'

They reversed and turned off into another avenue. Five minutes or so later they drew up at a newly dug grave. To one side was a heap of brown clayey soil and a couple of muddy spades.

Viktor got out. Surveying the scene, he saw a crowd of people about 50 metres away, and from the opposite direction, two skinny-looking cemetery hands in quilted jackets and trousers, both full of holes, were approaching.

'This the scientist?' asked one.

'Let's have him then,' said the other with a jerk of the head.

They lowered the coffin to the ground beside the grave. One fetched a coil of stout rope and arranged it for the lowering of the coffin.

Viktor slipped back to the bus, lifted Misha out, and set him down. The rope-arranger looked askance, but worked on.

'Poor sort of do, this, isn't it?' the other workman asked the driver. 'No priest, no palaver.'

The driver looked pointedly in Viktor's direction to shut him up.

Having lowered the coffin, the workmen turned expectantly to the man with the penguin.

Going to the graveside, Viktor dropped the flowers onto the coffin lid, followed by a handful of earth.

The workmen plied their spades and in ten minutes the grave was formed. They then went their way, each with a million tip in the inflated currency of the country, saying he should look them up in May, when the grave had settled. Cosmetician and undertaker departed in the bus, and Viktor, who had declined the offer of a lift to the entrance, was left alone with Misha.

Misha was standing stiffly by the grave, as though deep in thought, and looking across at the neighbouring funeral. Viktor found its intrusive noise more than a little irritating.

It was odd to be playing sole mourner. Where were the friends, the relatives? Or had Pidpaly outlived them? More than likely. And, but for Viktor's interest in penguins, who would there have been to bury him, and where?

Cheeks nipped by the cold, gloveless hands freezing, he looked about him. He had no idea how to find his way out, but he wasn't worried.

'Well Misha,' he sighed, stooping to the penguin's level, 'that's how we humans bury our dead.'

Wait

do not leave yet.
Let me rearrange the world
for you.

'Wait'
by Faraj Bou al-Isha,

from **A Crack in the Wall: New Arab Poetry**, edited by
Margaret Obank & Samuel Shimon
translated from Arabic by KHALED MATTAWA

"...I like a translation that has obviously been around, travelled a bit, lived a little. I like a translation that lets you see where it has come from, that precisely does not pretend that all over the world we all eat the same burgers in the same buns, but that in fact draws us into new places, new experiences...."

Michèle Roberts

Author's details

Isabel Allende was born in Peru and raised in Chile, which she fled after Pinochet's coup. She has published many acclaimed novels and two memoirs. She now lives in California.

Meg Bateman was born in Edinburgh in 1959 and lectures at Sabhal Mór Ostaig in Skye. She has published two collections of poetry and in 1997 won a Scottish Arts Council book award.

Geneviève Brisac was born in 1951 in Paris. She spent several years teaching before going into the world of publishing. She has worked as an editor of children's books and writes for the literary pages of *Le Monde*. *Losing Eugenio* is her fourth novel.

Emmanuel Carrère is one of France's most critically acclaimed authors. His novels include *The Moustache* and *Class Trip*, winner of the Prix Femina.

Mia Couto was born in 1955 in Mozambique and is the most prominent of the younger generation of writers in Portuguese-speaking Africa. He worked as a journalist for several years and is now an environmental biologist. *Under the Frangipani* is his first novel to be published in English.

Menna Elfyn has published six acclaimed books of poetry in Wales. She lives in Llandysul and is currently co-editing an anthology of 20th century Welsh verse.

Nikolaj Frobenius, born in 1965, studied film at the London Institute, and literature at the University of Oslo. He has worked as the editor of a literary magazine, and won the Anders Sahres Prize for Young Writers in 1997. *De Sade's Valet*, his third novel, has been published in ten countries, including France, Denmark, Germany and Italy.

Arnon Grunberg was born in Amsterdam in 1971. His first novel, *Blue Monday*, written for a dare, was a best-seller in Holland and translated into several languages. He lives in New York where he writes and works as a waiter.

Pedro Juan Gutiérrez began his working life at the age of eleven as an ice-cream vendor and newsboy. The author of several published works of poetry, he lives in Havana.

Judith Hermann is thirty and lives in Berlin. *The Summerhouse, Later* is her first book.

Ioana Ieronim was born in 1947 and worked as an editor for many years. In 1992 she became a diplomat and is now programme director for Fulbright US-Romanian exchanges in Bucharest.

Faraj Bou al-Isha was born in Libya in 1956, where he worked as a teacher and then a journalist before leaving for Cyprus in 1988. He has published three volumes of poetry and now lives as a political refugee in Germany.

Karin Kiwus, a very well-known poet and cultural figure in Germany, was born in Berlin in 1942.

Andrey Kurkov was born in St Petersburg in 1961 and now lives in Kiev. He studied at the Foreign Language Institute in Kiev and worked for some time as a journalist. He now writes screenplays, including of his own work, and has published four novels and four books for children.

Tessa de Loo's novels include *The Girls from the Sweet Factory*, *Meander* and *The Miracle of the Dog*, while *A Danger on the Way*, recently published, is a witty collection from her column for a Dutch motoring magazine. She lives in Portugal.

Dunya Mikhail was born in Baghdad in 1965. She studied English Literature at Baghdad University and has published three collections of poetry. She has lived in Michigan, USA, since 1996.

Walter Moers was born in 1957. A celebrated illustrator, cartoonist and novelist, he lives in Hamburg.

Marta Morazzoni was born in Milan in 1950 and teaches literature in a secondary school. She has written three novels and a volume of short stories, *Girl in a Turban*.

Haruki Murakami, born in Kyoto in 1949, is one of Japan's leading novelists. Apart from several novels, he has also published *Underground*, an exploration of the infamous Tokyo subway gas attack. In addition he has translated many English novels into Japanese, including the work of F. Scott Fitzgerald and Truman Capote.

Amos Oz was born in Jerusalem in 1939. An internationally acclaimed author, he has received many honours and awards including the Prix Femina, the Israel Prize and the Frankfurt Peace Prize. He lectures in literature at the Ben Gurion University of the Negev and lives in Arad, Israel.

Emine Sevgi Özdamar was born in Turkey in 1946, but has lived in Germany since 1976. She has published two collections of short stories and two novels and has received various awards, including the Ingeborg Bachmann Prize in 1991 and the Adalbert von Chamisso Prize in 1999.

Don Paterson was born in Dundee in 1963 and works as a musician and an editor. He has written two previous collections of poetry, *Nil Nil* and *God's Gift to Women*, the latter winning both the T.S. Eliot prize for 1997 and the Geoffrey Faber Memorial Prize.

Miklós Radnóti, one of the most talented young poets in 1930s Hungary, was born into a Budapest Jewish family in 1909. Although he converted to Catholicism in his youth, he was still persecuted as a Jew by the Nazis, serving three periods of forced labour throughout the war. He died in November 1944, in the western Hungarian town of Abda during a forced march.

Manuel Rivas was born in A Corûna in 1957. He writes in the Galician language of north-west Spain. An acclaimed novelist, he is also a journalist on *El País*. His collection of short stories, *Butterfly's Tongue*, has recently been made into a film.

Andreas Staïkos was born in 1944 and is a playwright and translator. He is Professor at the Institut Français d' Athènes and, he claims, an accomplished cook.

Antonio Tabucchi was born in Pisa in 1943 and now holds the Chair of Literature in the University of Siena. His novels have won many awards including the Italian PEN Club Prize and the European Aristeion prize. He has also translated Portuguese poet Fernando Pessoa into Italian.

Véronique Tadjo was born in Paris and grew up in the Côte d'Ivoire. She has published two collection of poems, three novels and several children's books. Her recent book, *L'Ombre d'Imana*, is on Rwanda and the genocide.

Rabindranath Tagore (1861–1941) received the Nobel Prize for literature in 1913. Although he wrote over forty books of poetry, *Gitanjali* or *Song Offerings* (1906–10) is his best-known work.

May Telmissany was born in Cairo in 1965. She has an MA in French Literature from the University of Cairo and is currently preparing a doctoral thesis at the University of Montreal. *Dunyazad* is her first novel.

Fernando Vallejo was born in Medellín, Colombia in 1942. He has directed three films, written several screenplays and novels. He is regarded as one of the first Latin American novelists to have broken with the tradition of 'magical realism'. *Our Lady of the Assassins* is his first novel to be translated into English.

Gao Xingjian was born in 1940. In the early 1980s he came to prominence for his experimental works of drama, fiction and theory, a prominence which soon brought him into conflict with the

Chinese Communist Party. Following the end of the Cultural Revolution he was able to publish his works more easily and travel abroad. However, in 1987 he left China to take up a fellowship in Germany, taking with him the manuscript of *Soul Mountain*, and resolved not to return. He now lives in Paris.

Translators' Details

Roger Allen is Professor of Arabic Language and Literature at the University of Pennsylvania. He has published many articles on Arabic literature and translated many Arabic works.

George Bird is the translator of Dostoevsky's *The Double*. In 1986 he won the Pluto Crime Prize for his novel *Death in Leningrad.*

David Brookshaw is Professor of Luso-Brazilian Studies at Bristol University. He has written widely on colonial and post-colonial writers in the Portuguese-speaking world and has translated the following works by Mia Couto: *Voices Made Night* (Heinemann, 1990), and *Every Man is a Race* (Heinemann, 1994).

John Brownjohn's translations include *Das Boot* ('The Boat') and Willy Brandt's *People and Politics*. He has won many translation awards, including the US PEN Goethe House Prize in 1981 and the Schlegel-Tieck Prize in 1995.

Gillian Clarke is a poet and teacher of creative writing. She has published seven volumes of poetry, including her Collected Poems (1997). She has also translated the Welsh novel *Tegwch y Bore* by Kate Roberts and a play commissioned for Theatre Powys, *The Time of the Wolf.*

Linda Coverdale has translated more than seventeen novels from French, including the work of Patrick Chamoiseau, Elisabeth Gille and Marie Darrieussecq.

Margot Bettauer Dembo is a freelance translator and editor who lives in New York. She won the Goethe-Institut/Berlin Translator's prize in 1994/95. Her recent translations include *Aftertime*, a novel by Olaf Georg Kelin, *The Triumph of Hope* by Ruth Elias, and *Europa, Europa* by Solomon Perel.

Jonathan Dunne has translated many Galician works including, with Margaret Jull Costa, Maunel Rivas' previous collection of short stories, *Butterfly's Tongue*.

Luise von Flotow translates literary work from German and French to English, and teaches translation studies at the University of Ottawa, Canada. She has published many French-Canadian writers in English translation, as well as Germans Herta Mueller, Thomas Brasch, Gabriele Eckart, Martin Walser and Gino Chiellino.

Sam Garrett has lived in Holland for twenty years. He has translated Tim Crabbe's *The Cave* and is at present working on Arnon Grunberg's new novel *Phantom Pain*.

Wangũi wa Goro is a social critic, researcher, writer and translator. Her translations include Ngũgĩ wa Thiong'o's novel *Matigari*. She is currently completing research in translation studies at Middlesex University.

Tom Geddes, formerly head of the Germanic Collections at the British Library, now a freelance translator, has translated many books from Nowegian and Swedish, including novels by Knut Hamsun, Jan Wiese, Lars Gustafsson and Torgny Lindgren, for whose *The Way of a Serpent* he received the inaugural Bernard Shaw Translation Prize in 1991.

Paul Hammond is a translator and writer, and an expert on the surrealists, particularly surrealist cinema. He is the translator of Michel Houellebecq's *Whatever* (Serpent's Tail 1998), author of *L'Age d'or* (British Film Institute, 1998) and *Constellations of Miró*, Breton (City Lights, 2000), and the editor of *The Shadow and its Shadow: Surrealist Writings on the Cinema* (City Lights, 2000). He lives in Barcelona.

Elin ap Hywel is a poet and translator. She has published two volumes of poetry and her work has also appeared in many anthologies and journals.

Francis R. Jones is recognized as one of Europe's leading poetry translators. He has twice won the European Poetry Translation Prize, as well as other prestigious awards. He teaches at the Newcastle University Language Centre.

Nicholas de Lange teaches in the theology faculty at Cambridge University and has translated many of Amos Oz's works into English.

Mabel Lee is Honorary Associate Professor in Chinese Studies at the University of Sydney.

Ruth Levitt's translation of the Dutch epic bestseller *The Twins* by Tessa de Loo was first published in 2000 (by Arcadia in the UK, Australia and New Zealand, and by Soho Press in the US), and attracted very positive critical reviews. She has published translations of other major Dutch and Flemish literary authors: *The Other Side* by Marga Minco (1994, Peter Owen) and *The Swordfish* by Hugo Claus (1996, Peter Owen).

Khaled Mattawa is a Libyan poet and translator. Born in 1964, he emigrated to the USA when he was fifteen and in 1988 he became the first Arab-American to win a Guggenheim Poetry Fellowship. He teaches in the English faculty at the University of Texas, Austin.

Christopher Middleton is a poet who has been translating poetry for more than forty years from a variety of languages including German, Swedish, and Turkish. *With Faint Harps and Silver Voices: Selected Translations*, he has become one of very few translators to have a selected work published.

J.C. Patrick translates many of Italy's foremost writers. Both his translations of Bufalino's *Blind Argus* and of Claudio Magris's *Danube* were awarded the John Florio Prize. He has also published several volumes of poetry. He lives in Tuscany.

Margaret Sayers Peden has translated many works from Spanish, including Isabel Allende's previous novel *Eva Luna* as well as the poetry of Pablo Neruda and Sor Juana Ines de la Cruz.

Emma Rose won the John Florio prize with the first book she translated, Marta Morazzoni's novel *His Mother's House*. She has also translated Sebastiano Vassalli's *The Swan*.

Jay Rubin is professor of Japanese literature at Harvard University. Apart from translating Murakami's novels into English, he has also written a critical study of the author.

Adam J. Sorkin is Professor of English at Penn State University. He has also translated Liliana Ursu.

Anne-Marie Stanton-Ife teaches English language and literature in Athens and works as a translator from Greek and Norwegian.

J.A. Underwood has translated many French and German authors including Gaston Bachelard, Sartre and Kafka. A former joint winner of the Schlegel-Tieck Prize for his new translation of Franz Kafka's *The Castle*, he is currently working as part of a team producing new versions of some of the works of Sigmund Freud.

Natasha Wimmer is the literary editor of the *American Scholar*. Her next translation project is *Letters to a Young Novelist*, by Mario Vargas Llosa. She lives in New York City.

Joe Winter taught English in London from 1967–94. He now lives in Calcutta where he is working on more translations of Tagore and the poems of Jibananada Das.

We would like to thank the following publishers for permission to include these extracts.

The complete list of titles featured is as follows:

Song Offerings by Rabindranath Tagore, translated by Joe Winter, published by Anvil Press, 2000.
Life is a Caravanserai • Has Two Doors • I Came In One • I Went Out The Other by Emine Sevgi Özdamar, translated by Luise von Flotow, published by Middlesex University Press, 2000.
An Tuil: Anthology of 20th Century Scottish Gaelic Verse, ed. Ronald Black, translated by various, published by Polygon, 1999.
Under the Frangipani by Mia Couto ©Editorial Caminho, SA, Lisboa, 1996. English translation ©2001 David Brookshaw, published by Serpent's Tail, 2001.
The Triumph of the Water Witch by Ioana Ieronim, translated by Adam J. Sorkin with the author, published by Bloodaxe Books, 2000.
Silent Extras by Arnon Grunberg, translated by Sam Garrett, published by Secker & Warburg, 2000. Reprinted by permission of The Random House Group Ltd.
Norwegian Wood by Haruki Murakami, translated by Jay Rubin, published by The Harvill Press, 2000. Reprinted by permission of Rogers, Coleridge and White.
The Eyes: A version of Antonio Machado by Don Paterson, published by Faber & Faber, 1999.
The Missing Head of Damasceno Monteiro by Antonio Tabucchi ©Giancomo Feltrinelli Editore, Milan, 1997. English translation by J.C. Patrick ©The Harvill Press, 2000.
Cusan Dyn Dall/Blind Man's Kiss by Menna Elfyn, translated by various, published by Bloodaxe Books, 2001
De Sade's Valet by Nikolaj Frobenius, translated by Tom Geddes, published by Marion Boyars Publishers, 2000.
The Twins by Tessa de Loo, translated by Ruth Levitt, published by Arcadia Books, 2000.
The Adversary: A True Story of Murder and Deception by Emmanuel

Carrère, translated by Linda Coverdale, published by Bloomsbury, 2001.

The Alphonse Courrier Affair by Marta Morazzoni Giancomo ©Longanesi & C, 1997. English translation by ©Emma Rose, 1999, 2000. Published by The Harvill Press, 2000.

The Same Sea by Amos Oz, translated by Nicholas de Lange with the author, published by Chatto & Windus, 2001. Used by permission of The Random House Group Ltd.

Camp Notebook by Miklós Radnóti, translated by Francis R. Jones, published by Arc, 2000.

Losing Eugenio by Geneviève Brisac, translated by J.A. Underwood, published by Marion Boyars Publishers, 1999.

Faint Harps and Silver Voices: Selected Translations by Christopher Middleton, published by Carcanet, 1999.

Les Liaisons Culinaires by Andreas Staïkos ©Agra/Stavros Petsopolous, 1997. English translation ©Anne-Marie Stanton-Ife, 1997. Published by The Harvill Press.

A Summerhouse, Later by Judith Hermann, translated by Margot Bettauer Dembo, published by Flamingo, forthcoming June 2002. Used by permission of HarperCollins Publishers Ltd.

Our Lady of the Assassins by Fernando Vallejo, translated by Paul Hammond, published by Serpent's Tail, 2001.

The Carpenter's Pencil by ©Manuel Rivas Manuel Rivas, 1998 and ©Grupo Santillana de Ediciones S.A, 1998. English translation ©Jonathan Dunne, 2001. Published by The Harvill Press.

A Crack in the Wall: New Arab Poetry, edited by Margaret Obank & Samuel Shimon, translated by various, published by Saqi Books, 2000.

The 13½ Lives of Captain Bluebear by Walter Moers, translated by John Brownjohn, published by Martin Secker & Warburg, 2000. Reprinted by permission of The Random House Group Ltd.

Soul Mountain by Gao Xingjian, translated by Mabel Lee, published by Flamingo, 2001. Used by permission of HarperCollins Publishers Ltd.

Portrait in Sepia by Isabel Allende, translated by Margaret Sayers Peden, published by Flamingo, forthcoming October 2001. Used by permission of HarperCollins Publishers Ltd.

Dirty Havana Trilogy by Pedro Juan Gutiérrez , translated by Natasha

Wimmer, published by Faber & Faber, 2001

As the Crow Flies by Véronique Tadjo, translated by Wangüi wa Goro, 2001. Reprinted by permission of Heinemann Educational Publishers.

Dunyazad by May Telmissany, translated by Roger Allen, published by Saqi Books, 2000.

Death and the Penguin by Andrey Kurkov ©Andrey Kurkov, 1996 & ©Diogenes Verlag AG, Zurich, 1999. English translation translated ©George Bird, 2001. Published by The Harvill Press.

Editors' Details

Michèle Roberts is the author of ten novels including *Daughters of the House* (1992) which won the W H Smith Literary Award and was shortlisted for the Booker Prize. She has published two volumes of short stories, most recently *Playing Sardines*, and a collection of poetry, *All the Selves I Was*. Half-English and half-French, Michèle Roberts lives in London and in Mayenne, France. This year she is one of the Booker Prize judges.

Josephine Balmer has published two volumes of translations, *Sappho:Poems* and *Fragments* (Bloodaxe, 1992) and *Classical Women Poets* (Bloodaxe, 1996). Single translations and poems have also appeared in a wide range of anthologies, journals and newspapers, as well as been broadcast on several national radio networks. She has written extensively on translation and poetry for a number of publications including the *Independent*, the *Independent on Sunday*, the *Observer*, the *Financial Times*, the *Times Literary Supplement* and the *New Statesman*. She is currently working on a new version of Catullus.